Language Lessons
for a Living Education

MASTERBOOKS®
CURRICULUM

MASTER BOOKS
—CURRICULUM—

Author: Kristen Pratt

Master Books Creative Team:

Editor: Laura Welch

Design: Jennifer Bauer

Cover Design: Diana Bogardus

Copy Editors:
Judy Lewis
Willow Meek

Curriculum Review:
Kristen Pratt
Laura Welch
Diana Bogardus

First printing: March 2020
Third printing: August 2020

ISBN: 978-1-68344-211-0
ISBN: 978-1-61458-738-5 (digital)

Unless otherwise noted, Scripture quotations are taken from the New American Standard Bible® (NASB). Copyright © 1960, 1962, 1963, 1968, 1971, 1972, 1973, 1975, 1977, 1995 by The Lockman Foundation. Used by permission. www.Lockman.org.

Printed in the United States of America

Please visit our website for other great titles:
www.masterbooks.com

About the Author:

Kristen Pratt works as an author and Curriculum Editor for Master Books, where she has been writing curriculum and consulting for the past eight years. She has been homeschooling her nine children for over twenty years, having graduated five so far from high school. She has helped thousands of homeschool families navigate curriculum choices through her own curriculum business and now through the Master Books® communities online and via the app.

All images shutterstock.com or istockphotos.com unless indicated.

Pages 15, 30, 41, 51, 60, 65, 71, 78, 89, 91, 110, 115, 120, 136, 145: from *Not Too Small at All*, courtesy of Master Books; Page 77: Public Domain; Pages 175, 180, 182, 187, 188, 193, 203, 209, 219: from *Charlie & Trike*, courtesy of Master Books.

Scope and Sequence

4 ▸ Using This Course

11 ▸ Daily Schedule

23 ▸ Lesson 1 — Reading, Sight Words, Phonics: *sp, tw, wh, mb, ck, ng, nk*; Alphabet, Vowels, Phonics Fun!, Create Your Own Dictionary!

37 ▸ Lesson 2 — Picture Study, Reading, Sight Words, Phonics: *sh, ch, qu, ph, dd, ff, ll, ss, tt, zz*; Alphabet, Short and Long Vowels, Picture Study, Phonics Fun!, Create Your Own Dictionary!

49 ▸ Lesson 3 — Reading, Sight Words, Phonics: *th, kn, lf, lk, y*; Alphabet, Long and Short Vowels, Picture Study, Phonics Fun!, Create Your Own Dictionary!

63 ▸ Lesson 4 — Bible Reading, Reading, Sight Words, Phonics: *ea*; Alphabet, Vowel Sounds, Picture Study, Phonics Fun!, Create Your Own Dictionary!

73 ▸ Lesson 5 — Reading, Sight Words, Phonics: *gh*; Let's Write, Picture Study, Spelling, Nouns, Create Your Own Dictionary!

85 ▸ Lesson 6 — Picture Study, Reading, Sight Words, Phonics: *bl, cl, fl, gl, pl, sl*; Silent-e, Picture Study, Spelling, Nouns, Create Your Own Dictionary!

99 ▸ Lesson 7 — Reading, Sight Words, Phonics: *br, cr, dr, fr, gr, pr, tr, wr*; Silent Vowels, Long Vowels, Picture Study, Spelling, Nouns, Create Your Own Dictionary!

111 ▸ Lesson 8 — Poetry, Reading, Sight Words, Phonics: *ie*; Picture Study, Spelling, Nouns and Verbs, Create Your Own Dictionary!

123 ▸ Lesson 9 — Reading, Sight Words, Phonics: *ei*; Picture Study, Spelling, Nouns and Verbs, Create Your Own Dictionary!

133 ▸ Lesson 10 — Reading, Sight Words, Phonics: *oy*; Picture Study, Spelling, Nouns, Verbs, and Adjectives, Create Your Own Dictionary!

143 ▸ Lesson 11 — Picture Study, Reading, Sight Words, Phonics: *ou, ow*; Rule Breakers, Picture Study, Spelling, Nouns, Verbs and Adjectives, Create Your Own Dictionary!

153 ▸ Lesson 12 — Reading, Sight Words, Phonics: *oo*; Picture Study, Spelling, Nouns, Verbs, and Adjectives, Create Your Own Dictionary!

161 ▸ Lesson 13 — Bible Reading, Reading, Sight Words, Phonics: *ew*; Picture Study, Spelling, Nouns, Verbs, and Adjectives, Create Your Own Dictionary!

171 ▸ Lesson 14 — Reading, Sight Words, Phonics: *ou*; Punctuation, Picture Study, Sentences, Create Your Own Dictionary!

181 ▸ Lesson 15 — Picture Study, Reading, Sight Words, Phonics: *sc, sk, sl, sm, sn, sp, st, sw*; Capitalization, Punctuation, Picture Study, Sentences, Create Your Own Dictionary!

195 ▸ Lesson 16 — Reading, Sight Words, Phonics: *al, au, aw, ay, ai, ea, oa, oe, ee*; Capitalization, Punctuation, Picture Study, Sentences, Create Your Own Dictionary!

209 ▸ Lesson 17 — Poetry, Reading, Sight Words, Phonics: *str, spr, scr, spl*; Capitalization, Punctuation, Picture Study, Sentences, Create Your Own Dictionary!

221 ▸ Lesson 18 — Reading, Sight Words, Phonics: *squ, thr, dge, tch*; Capitalization, Punctuation, Picture Study, Sentences, Create Your Own Dictionary!

233 ▸ Teacher Aids

Features: The suggested weekly schedule enclosed has easy-to-manage lessons that guide the reading, worksheets, and all assessments. The pages of this guide are perforated and three-hole punched so materials are easy to tear out, hand out, grade, and store. Teachers are encouraged to adjust the schedule and materials needed in order to best work within their unique educational program.

Words to Sentences: It's time to move beyond phonetic sounds and individual words to laying the groundwork for reading and writing. Encouraging and fun lessons combine with solid basics to help your student develop both an enduring love for reading and stronger writing skills. He or she will learn to put together the puzzle of simple words into short sentences to successfully communicate on paper. Gentle, helpful guidance helps both the teacher and student as they begin a wonderful journey with new words and writing opportunities in a powerful language arts series!

🕐	**Approximately 20 to 30 minutes per lesson, five days a week**
🔑	**Includes answer keys for worksheets**
✏️	**Worksheets provided each week for lessons and template pages for the student dictionary**
	Designed for first grade in a one-semester or one-year course
🔁	**Pre-requisite — *Foundations Phonics* or other basic phonics course. Students should be reading CVC words and beginning sight words.**

Course Objectives: Students completing this course will:

- Learn the basics of reading, progressing from the foundations of phonics
- Study letters and words, discovering how they symbolize meaning
- Write out words, building up to sentences over the semester
- Create their own dictionaries from words learned each week
- Identify words in the books they learn to read through the semester
- Gain an appreciation of reading, writing, and basic communication

Course Description

Students who have completed our *Foundations Phonics* course (or another phonics course) will be ready to start this course. Students will practice reading while reviewing trickier vowel sounds and blends. They will also practice writing words and sentences. The foundations of writing are also laid through picture study, fostering an awareness of details and the ability to communicate them.

This course was designed to be flexible. We suggest using this course in one of two ways. Complete *Foundations Phonics* in the first half of first grade and this course in the second half. This is the preferred method for a gentle introduction to reading. We have designed this course around this schedule.

We have also included an alternative schedule for students who have completed *Foundations Phonics* in kindergarten and want to use this course in first grade. Both schedules are provided. Please adapt this course to meet the needs of your student. Note that the alternate schedule days do not match the days on the worksheets.

We have used two books as the foundation for this course: *Not Too Small at All* by Stephanie Z. Townsend and *Charlie and Trike in the Grand Canyon Adventure* by Ken Ham with Karen Hansel. The third book, *The Door of Salvation* by Ken Ham, is a fun book meant to encourage a student's desire to read. It is assigned near the end of the course as a fun way to practice reading skills and to celebrate all the student has accomplished. All three books are published by Master Books and are required.

On the fifth day of each week, there is a Create Your Own Dictionary! activity where the student writes out and illustrates words primarily from the books he or she is learning to read. The appendix has pages A to Z, as well as reproducible pages, so the student can continue making his or her own personal dictionary long after the course is over!

Required Course Materials:
This course has an integrated reading component that uses *Not Too Small at All*, *Charlie and Trike in the Grand Canyon Adventure*, and *The Door of Salvation*, all available from Master Books.

A Note from the Author

This series was written with inspiration from classic educators like Charlotte Mason and Emma Serl. It was also inspired by homeschool educators like David Marks, Angela O'Dell, Katherine (Loop) Hannon, and my colleagues Craig Froman and Laura Welch. If you could put these people in a room, you would find they all have different thoughts on how to educate a child, yet they have all taught me something that has gone into this series. I have taken the effective principles from long ago and updated them for a modern world with the hope of inspiring a new generation to communicate their faith and the gospel to their generation.

Thank you to Craig Froman, who developed the Create Your Own Dictionary! concept. Also, thank you to Diana Bogardus for creating the cover, which set the tone and beautiful feel of this course. Thank you to Jennifer Bauer for the hours of design work to marry function with beauty. Thank you to Laura Welch and the proofers for their insight and wisdom.

I am indebted to the Moms of Master Books, who give us valuable feedback on how to improve our curriculum to meet their needs. We do this for them and their children. It is our goal to come alongside them and provide the tools so that they can bring up a godly generation, known by the Lord. When the days feel long, I think of the impact our work is having on homeschooled children, and my strength is renewed. Thank you for allowing us to partner with you in the education of your children.

Of course, my children have for many years taught me principles of education that have surprised and inspired me. I have often marveled that nine children can grow up in the same home and be so different from each other. We truly are wonderfully and fearfully made. I have learned that curriculum needs to be flexible to meet the needs of the unique individuals God has entrusted to our care.

May God bless and keep you and give you wisdom and strength as you homeschool your children in the nurture and admonition of the Lord.

Blessings,

Kristen Pratt

About This Course

Teaching your student to read well is an exciting time. In this course, the student will build on what he or she has learned in *Foundations Phonics*. The student will continue to learn more about phonetic sounds, strengthen his or her writing skills, and learn some basic grammar concepts.

Students enjoy patterns. They like to have rhythms in life that they can count on. This course is set up in a pattern that students and teachers alike can rely on.

The first day of the weekly schedule includes reading from *Not Too Small at All, Charlie and Trike in the Grand Canyon Adventure,* and *The Door of Salvation.* Every other week includes a special feature such as a picture study, poem, or Scripture passage. The student also studies sight words and begins the independent reading for the week.

On the second day, the student will review and cover new phonics sounds. He or she will also practice writing. This may feel like a longer day than the others. Let the student's ability and stamina be the guide. Take breaks as needed. Save some of the work for the next day if needed.

Day three brings more phonics review and the ability to apply what he or she has learned. The student also engages in picture study, which helps strengthen attention to detail. The spelling words are introduced this day.

On the fourth day, the student has fun with words through spelling, grammar, and learning about sentences.

On the fifth day, the student will focus on reading, spelling, and vocabulary through creating his or her own dictionary.

A student's abilities and stamina can vary widely. While we have provided a Daily Schedule, feel free to adjust the pace according to the needs of your student. We have also given varied types of material in the back of the book to aid in the extra practice of key concepts.

We encourage the teacher to read through the Teacher Notes and lesson before beginning each lesson with the student.

We hope you enjoy using this course with your student. It is designed to foster a partnership between student and teacher, with the student gradually taking a lead role. Allowing the student's growing abilities, stamina, and interests to set the pace will allow his or her confidence to strengthen. This confidence is the key that will help unlock communication success.

Teaching Helps

We start students off reading out of real books because it inspires a love of reading. The skill of reading should not be isolated to random words and sentences on a boring page. Real excitement begins when students can read from a real book that connects them to a story and pictures.

We suggest allowing your student to read the words he or she is confident with and giving help with new words. When a new or difficult word is presented in a passage, help the student sound out the word. Give them help and quickly move on. This will encourage the student to face new words with confidence rather than stress.

When a student struggles with a word, read it for him or her. Review it once or twice, repeating the word while following it with your finger, and then cheerily move on. Another method is to place a piece of paper under the line that the student is reading. This also may be done under the line the teacher is reading as the student follows along. We suggest pointing to each word as it is read to the student.

If a student is struggling to read, sometimes his or her short-term memory needs to be developed. Reading is memory intensive. The student must remember the start of a word while sounding out the end. The student also must remember what he or she read in the first part of the sentence while reading the end of it. He or she also must remember the sequence of events within the story. There is a lot to remember, especially when the student is concentrating on words he or she does not know. You can work on increasing short-term memory through memory games. You will find one in the back of the book.

You will find fun, colorful images used to illustrate words the student is working with. Please name the words before the student begins their work.

Reading should be a fun activity rather than one filled with worry over performance. Enjoy the process with your student!

The student's vocabulary is expanded by creating their own dictionary. We have chosen words the student may encounter in their books and are concrete in nature. The weekly spelling words may be substituted if desired.

This course uses the sight word list from Master Books *Foundations Phonics*, which is provided in the back of the book. Sight word flashcards can also be purchased from various companies for even more sight word practice if needed.

The beginnings of writing are also part of this course. Be sure the student has a proper grasp of the pencil, good posture, and a solid writing surface. Spend time watching your student write letters and words, making sure he or she is writing the letters in the correct way. Please see illustration in the back of the book.

We have provided the alphabet letters in the back of the book for additional practice. You may make copies or put the page in a plastic sleeve (or laminate it) for use with dry erase markers. If the student needs extra practice with words and sentences, we recommend having the student pick words out of the books he or she is reading and write them on lined paper meant for young students. Have the student build up to writing sentences.

We also suggest the love of writing be encouraged by allowing the student to write his or her own sentences. Encourage story writing and letter writing as a way for the student to connect with the writing process. The student may enjoy drawing a picture and writing a few words or sentences under his or her drawing. Notebooks with space for drawing and lines underneath to tell the story are a great resource to have on hand for this activity.

When this course is completed, we encourage instructors to continue to encourage the love of reading through real books. Master Books publishes a variety of books that are very engaging and purposeful.

Select books that are appropriate to the student's age and ability level and read them with him or her. Help the student sound out words he or she is stuck on. Continue to join the student in reading, gradually weaning him or her toward independence.

Stories, Poems, Scripture

The stories, poems, and Scripture passages may be co-read by the student and the teacher. Let the ability of the student be the guide. All questions following the stories, poems, and Scripture should be read by the teacher and answered orally by the student.

If the student struggles to narrate, or tell back the story, a simple question or hint may be given. Telling back the story helps the student build memory skills.

The NASB is used for all Scripture passages (unless otherwise noted) in this book, but you may use the version you prefer.

Independent Reading

Work with the student to pick simple books for him or her to read out loud to the teacher daily. Care should be taken to select books within the student's reading ability. The books should gradually increase in length and difficulty.

You will find in the back of this book suggestions and a place to record the books the student has read or plans to read.

Oral Narration

Oral narration (or telling back) helps the student develop listening skills and reading comprehension. The student is encouraged to tell back the story in his or her own words. If the student struggles, the teacher may ask some guided questions. The goal is to gradually wean the student from the prompts until the story can be retold without them.

Phonics

This course was designed to continue the reading journey established in *Foundations Phonics*. If another phonics course has been used, the student should know how to read short words and beginning sight words. They should be able to read a short sentence.

Students will learn a variety of blends and sounds to strengthen their reading skills. We suggest co-reading, allowing the student to read words and sentences that are within his or her abilities. We have also included in this book the sentences the student is to read out of the assigned book. We have added phonetic markings for those students who need the extra clues.

Please note: Pronunciations can vary by region. Please adjust the phonetic markings according to the pronunciations used by your family.

Keep in mind that students range widely in reading ability, stamina, and pace. Encourage every effort the student makes. Be sure to provide plenty of extra reading practice through simple books you have at home. You may want to add phonetic markings to the books if needed. Study the phonetic helps in the back of the book as often as needed.

Spelling

Spelling is woven throughout the course, but starting in week 5, it is the focus of Days 3 and 4. The spelling words are introduced on Day 3, and more practice is given on Day 4.

For those who enjoy word boxes, you can find them on our website: www.masterbooks.com/classroom-aids. **Note:** For Lessons 14–18, we have used our chosen words. You may want to review them with your student before he or she attempts the word boxes for those lessons.

The student will work with a new set of words when creating his or her own dictionary, giving the student more experience with spelling.

The student is just beginning his or her journey with words. Allow the student to enjoy learning how to spell words rather than being overly concerned with mastery.

Create Your Own Dictionary!

The student will create his or her very own dictionary, developing reading, spelling, and vocabulary skills.

The teacher will need to make copies of the Create Your Own Dictionary! sheets in the back of the book as needed. They are also available for download on our website, masterbooks.com.

If the student struggles to add all the words to his or her dictionary, the teacher may let him or her pick fewer words. Let the student's ability and stamina be the guide.

The student will write out the word, draw a picture, and then give a simple one- to three-word definition.

The student is encouraged to remove the dictionary pages and continue to add words to it long after he or she has finished the course. The teacher may offer blank Create Your Own Dictionary! pages for this purpose.

For Fun!

"Just 4 Fun!" activities provide extra critical thinking, problem-solving, and handwriting practice. They are meant to be a fun break from the regular lesson. If the student has difficulty completing an activity, offer hints and encouragement. Answers are provided in the answer key as part of the lesson's answers.

Teacher Aids

In the back of the book, you will find a section of Teacher Aids. These aids include assessments, extra practice pages, study sheets, fun games, and more. We encourage you to look through the tools provided to use with your student. They provide opportunities for enrichment and fun games to hone skills as your student learns how to read and communicate more effectively.

Handwriting

While this is not a formal handwriting course, each time the student writes, it is an opportunity to practice handwriting. It is good to remind your student to write neatly, using his or her best penmanship. We also suggest using Scripture as copywork for handwriting practice. Use the student's ability and stamina as a guide. We suggest starting with short sentences and working up to longer ones.

Assessment

An assessment chart is provided in the back of the book in the Teacher Aids section. It may be used for assigning grades.

One Semester Suggested Daily Schedule

Date	Day	Assignment	Due Date	✓	Grade
		First Semester-First Quarter			
Week 1	Day 1	Read Together • Page 23 Complete Lesson 1 Exercise 1 • Pages 24–26			
	Day 2	Complete Lesson 1 Exercise 2 • Pages 27–31			
	Day 3	Complete Lesson 1 Exercise 3 • Pages 32–33			
	Day 4	Complete Lesson 1 Exercise 4 • Pages 34–35			
	Day 5	Complete Lesson 1 Exercise 5 • Page 36			
Week 2	Day 6	Picture Study • Page 37 Complete Lesson 2 Exercise 1 • Page 38			
	Day 7	Complete Lesson 2 Exercise 2 • Pages 39–43			
	Day 8	Complete Lesson 2 Exercise 3 • Pages 44–45			
	Day 9	Complete Lesson 2 Exercise 4 • Pages 46–47			
	Day 10	Complete Lesson 2 Exercise 5 • Page 48			
Week 3	Day 11	Read Together • Page 49 Complete Lesson 3 Exercise 1 • Page 50			
	Day 12	Complete Lesson 3 Exercise 2 • Pages 51–55			
	Day 13	Complete Lesson 3 Exercise 3 • Pages 56–59			
	Day 14	Complete Lesson 3 Exercise 4 • Pages 60–61			
	Day 15	Complete Lesson 3 Exercise 5 • Page 62			
Week 4	Day 16	Read Bible • Page 63 Complete Lesson 4 Exercise 1 • Page 64			
	Day 17	Complete Lesson 4 Exercise 2 • Pages 65–67			
	Day 18	Complete Lesson 4 Exercise 3 • Page 68			
	Day 19	Complete Lesson 4 Exercise 4 • Pages 69–71			
	Day 20	Complete Lesson 4 Exercise 5 • Page 72			
Week 5	Day 21	Read Together • Page 73 Complete Lesson 5 Exercise 1 • Page 73			
	Day 22	Complete Lesson 5 Exercise 2 • Pages 74–77			
	Day 23	Complete Lesson 5 Exercise 3 • Pages 78–79			
	Day 24	Complete Lesson 5 Exercise 4 • Pages 80–83			
	Day 25	Complete Lesson 5 Exercise 5 • Page 84			
Week 6	Day 26	Picture Study • Page 85 Complete Lesson 6 Exercise 1 • Page 86			
	Day 27	Complete Lesson 6 Exercise 2 • Pages 87–91			
	Day 28	Complete Lesson 6 Exercise 3 • Pages 92–93			
	Day 29	Complete Lesson 6 Exercise 4 • Pages 94–96			
	Day 30	Complete Lesson 6 Exercise 5 • Pages 97–98			

Date	Day	Assignment	Due Date	✓	Grade
Week 7	Day 31	Read Together • Page 99 Complete Lesson 7 Exercise 1 • Page 99			
	Day 32	Complete Lesson 7 Exercise 2 • Pages 100–104			
	Day 33	Complete Lesson 7 Exercise 3 • Pages 105–106			
	Day 34	Complete Lesson 7 Exercise 4 • Pages 107–109			
	Day 35	Complete Lesson 7 Exercise 5 • Page 110			
Week 8	Day 36	Read Poem • Page 111 Complete Lesson 8 Exercise 1 • Pages 112–113			
	Day 37	Complete Lesson 8 Exercise 2 • Pages 114–116			
	Day 38	Complete Lesson 8 Exercise 3 • Pages 117–118			
	Day 39	Complete Lesson 8 Exercise 4 • Pages 119–121			
	Day 40	Complete Lesson 8 Exercise 5 • Page 122			
Week 9	Day 41	Read Together • Page 123 Complete Lesson 9 Exercise 1 • Page 123			
	Day 42	Complete Lesson 9 Exercise 2 • Pages 124–126			
	Day 43	Complete Lesson 9 Exercise 3 • Pages 127–128			
	Day 44	Complete Lesson 9 Exercise 4 • Pages 129–131			
	Day 45	Complete Lesson 9 Exercise 5 • Page 132			
First Semester-Second Quarter					
Week 1	Day 46	Read Together • Page 133 Complete Lesson 10 Exercise 1 • Page 133			
	Day 47	Complete Lesson 10 Exercise 2 • Pages 134–135			
	Day 48	Complete Lesson 10 Exercise 3 • Page 136			
	Day 49	Complete Lesson 10 Exercise 4 • Pages 137–140			
	Day 50	Complete Lesson 10 Exercise 5 • Pages 141–142			
Week 2	Day 51	Picture Study • Page 143 Complete Lesson 11 Exercise 1 • Page 144	'		
	Day 52	Complete Lesson 11 Exercise 2 • Pages 145–146			
	Day 53	Complete Lesson 11 Exercise 3 • Pages 147–148			
	Day 54	Complete Lesson 11 Exercise 4 • Pages 149–151			
	Day 55	Complete Lesson 11 Exercise 5 • Page 152			
Week 3	Day 56	Read Together • Page 153 Complete Lesson 12 Exercise 1 • Page 153			
	Day 57	Complete Lesson 12 Exercise 2 • Pages 154–155			
	Day 58	Complete Lesson 12 Exercise 3 • Page 156			
	Day 59	Complete Lesson 12 Exercise 4 • Pages 157–159			
	Day 60	Complete Lesson 12 Exercise 5 • Page 160			
Week 4	Day 61	Read Bible • Page 161 Complete Lesson 13 Exercise 1 • Page 162			
	Day 62	Complete Lesson 13 Exercise 2 • Pages 163–165			
	Day 63	Complete Lesson 13 Exercise 3 • Page 166			
	Day 64	Complete Lesson 13 Exercise 4 • Pages 167–169			
	Day 65	Complete Lesson 13 Exercise 5 • Page 170			

Date	Day	Assignment	Due Date	✓	Grade
Week 5	Day 66	Read Together • Page 171 Complete Lesson 14 Exercise 1 • Pages 172–173			
	Day 67	Complete Lesson 14 Exercise 2 • Pages 174–175			
	Day 68	Complete Lesson 14 Exercise 3 • Pages 176–178			
	Day 69	Complete Lesson 14 Exercise 4 • Page 179			
	Day 70	Complete Lesson 14 Exercise 5 • Page 180			
Week 6	Day 71	Picture Study • Page 181 Complete Lesson 15 Exercise 1 • Pages 182–183			
	Day 72	Complete Lesson 15 Exercise 2 • Pages 184–187			
	Day 73	Complete Lesson 15 Exercise 3 • Pages 188–190			
	Day 74	Complete Lesson 15 Exercise 4 • Pages 191–193			
	Day 75	Complete Lesson 15 Exercise 5 • Page 194			
Week 7	Day 76	Read Together • Page 195 Complete Lesson 16 Exercise 1 • Page 196			
	Day 77	Complete Lesson 16 Exercise 2 • Pages 197–201			
	Day 78	Complete Lesson 16 Exercise 3 • Pages 202–204			
	Day 79	Complete Lesson 16 Exercise 4 • Pages 205–207			
	Day 80	Complete Lesson 16 Exercise 5 • Page 208			
Week 8	Day 81	Read Poem • Page 209 Complete Lesson 17 Exercise 1 • Pages 210–211			
	Day 82	Complete Lesson 17 Exercise 2 • Pages 212–214			
	Day 83	Complete Lesson 17 Exercise 3 • Pages 215–217			
	Day 84	Complete Lesson 17 Exercise 4 • Pages 218–219			
	Day 85	Complete Lesson 17 Exercise 5 • Page 220			
Week 9	Day 86	Read Together • Page 221 Complete Lesson 18 Exercise 1 • Page 221			
	Day 87	Complete Lesson 18 Exercise 2 • Pages 222–224			
	Day 88	Complete Lesson 18 Exercise 3 • Pages 225–227			
	Day 89	Complete Lesson 18 Exercise 4 • Pages 228–229			
	Day 90	Complete Lesson 18 Exercise 5 • Page 230			
		Final Grade			

Alternate One-Year Daily Schedule — First Semester

Date	Day	Assignment	Due Date	✓	Grade
		First Semester-First Quarter			
Week 1	Day 1	Read Together • Page 23 Complete Lesson 1 Exercise 1 • Pages 24–26			
	Day 2				
	Day 3	Begin Lesson 1 Exercise 2 • Pages 27–29			
	Day 4				
	Day 5	Complete Lesson 1 Exercise 2 • Pages 30–31			
Week 2	Day 6	Complete Lesson 1 Exercise 3 • Pages 32–33			
	Day 7				
	Day 8	Complete Lesson 1 Exercise 4 • Pages 34–35			
	Day 9				
	Day 10	Complete Lesson 1 Exercise 5 • Page 36			
Week 3	Day 11	Picture Study • Page 37 Complete Lesson 2 Exercise 1 • Page 38			
	Day 12				
	Day 13	Begin Lesson 2 Exercise 2 • Pages 39–42 (stop after problem 10)			
	Day 14				
	Day 15	Complete Lesson 2 Exercise 2 • Pages 42–43 (Let's Sing and Let's Write)			
Week 4	Day 16	Complete Lesson 2 Exercise 3 • Pages 44–45			
	Day 17				
	Day 18	Complete Lesson 2 Exercise 4 • Pages 46–47			
	Day 19				
	Day 20	Complete Lesson 2 Exercise 5 • Page 48			
Week 5	Day 21	Read Together • Page 49 Complete Lesson 3 Exercise 1 • Page 50			
	Day 22				
	Day 23	Begin Lesson 3 Exercise 2 • Pages 51–53			
	Day 24				
	Day 25	Complete Lesson 3 Exercise 2 • Pages 54–55			
Week 6	Day 26	Complete Lesson 3 Exercise 3 • Pages 56–59			
	Day 27				
	Day 28	Complete Lesson 3 Exercise 4 • Pages 60–61			
	Day 29				
	Day 30	Complete Lesson 3 Exercise 5 • Page 62			
Week 7	Day 31	Read Bible • Page 63 Complete Lesson 4 Exercise 1 • Page 64			
	Day 32				
	Day 33	Complete Lesson 4 Exercise 2 • Pages 65–67			
	Day 34				
	Day 35	Complete Lesson 4 Exercise 3 • Page 68			

Date	Day	Assignment	Due Date	✓	Grade
Week 8	Day 36	Complete Lesson 4 Exercise 4 • Pages 69–71			
	Day 37				
	Day 38	Complete Lesson 4 Exercise 5 • Page 72			
	Day 39				
	Day 40	Review Course Assessment Chart; review lessons if student still needs to master the skill. Teacher aids are available in the back of the book.			
Week 9	Day 41	Read Together • Page 73 Complete Lesson 5 Exercise 1 • Page 73			
	Day 42				
	Day 43	Complete Lesson 5 Exercise 2 • Pages 74–77			
	Day 44				
	Day 45	Complete Lesson 5 Exercise 3 • Pages 78–79			
First Semester-Second Quarter					
Week 1	Day 46	Begin Lesson 5 Exercise 4 • Pages 80–81			
	Day 47				
	Day 48	Complete Lesson 5 Exercise 4 • Pages 82–83			
	Day 49				
	Day 50	Complete Lesson 5 Exercise 5 • Page 84			
Week 2	Day 51	Picture Study • Page 85 Complete Lesson 6 Exercise 1 • Page 86			
	Day 52				
	Day 53	Begin Lesson 6 Exercise 2 • Pages 87–89			
	Day 54				
	Day 55	Complete Lesson 6 Exercise 2 • Pages 90–91			
Week 3	Day 56	Complete Lesson 6 Exercise 3 • Pages 92–93			
	Day 57				
	Day 58	Begin Lesson 6 Exercise 4 • Pages 94–95			
	Day 59				
	Day 60	Complete Lesson 6 Exercise 4 • Page 96			
Week 4	Day 61	Complete Lesson 6 Exercise 5 • Pages 97–98			
	Day 62				
	Day 63	Read Together • Page 99 Complete Lesson 7 Exercise 1 • Page 99			
	Day 64				
	Day 65	Begin Lesson 7 Exercise 2 • Pages 100–103 (stop after problem 8)			
Week 5	Day 66	Complete Lesson 7 Exercise 2 • Pages 103–104 (Let's Write)			
	Day 67				
	Day 68	Complete Lesson 7 Exercise 3 • Pages 105–106			
	Day 69				
	Day 70	Complete Lesson 7 Exercise 4 • Pages 107–109			

Date	Day	Assignment	Due Date	✓	Grade
Week 6	Day 71	Complete Lesson 7 Exercise 5 • Page 110			
	Day 72				
	Day 73	Read Poem • Page 111 Complete Lesson 8 Exercise 1 • Pages 112–113			
	Day 74				
	Day 75	Complete Lesson 8 Exercise 2 • Pages 114–116			
Week 7	Day 76	Complete Lesson 8 Exercise 3 • Pages 117–118			
	Day 77				
	Day 78	Complete Lesson 8 Exercise 4 • Pages 119–121			
	Day 79				
	Day 80	Complete Lesson 8 Exercise 5 • Page 122			
Week 8	Day 81	Review Course Assessment Chart; review lessons if student still needs to master the skill. Teacher aids are available in the back of the book.			
	Day 82				
	Day 83	Read Together • Page 123 Complete Lesson 9 Exercise 1 • Page 123			
	Day 84				
	Day 85	Complete Lesson 9 Exercise 2 • Pages 124–126			
Week 9	Day 86	Complete Lesson 9 Exercise 3 • Pages 127–128			
	Day 87				
	Day 88	Complete Lesson 9 Exercise 4 • Pages 129–131			
	Day 89				
	Day 90	Complete Lesson 9 Exercise 5 • Page 132			
		Mid-Term Grade			

Alternate One-Year Daily Schedule — Second Semester

Date	Day	Assignment	Due Date	✓	Grade
		Second Semester-Third Quarter			
Week 1	Day 91	Read Together • Page 133 Complete Lesson 10 Exercise 1 • Page 133			
	Day 92				
	Day 93	Complete Lesson 10 Exercise 2 • Pages 134–135			
	Day 94				
	Day 95	Complete Lesson 10 Exercise 3 • Page 136			
Week 2	Day 96	Complete Lesson 10 Exercise 4 • Pages 137–140			
	Day 97				
	Day 98	Complete Lesson 10 Exercise 5 • Pages 141–142			
	Day 99				
	Day 100	Picture Study • Page 143 Complete Lesson 11 Exercise 1 • Page 144			
Week 3	Day 101	Complete Lesson 11 Exercise 2 • Pages 145–146			
	Day 102				
	Day 103	Complete Lesson 11 Exercise 3 • Pages 147–148			
	Day 104				
	Day 105	Complete Lesson 11 Exercise 4 • Pages 149–151			
Week 4	Day 106	Complete Lesson 11 Exercise 5 • Page 152			
	Day 107				
	Day 108	Read Together • Page 153 Complete Lesson 12 Exercise 1 • Page 153			
	Day 109				
	Day 110	Complete Lesson 12 Exercise 2 • Pages 154–155			
Week 5	Day 111	Complete Lesson 12 Exercise 3 • Page 156			
	Day 112				
	Day 113	Begin Lesson 12 Exercise 4 • Pages 157–158			
	Day 114				
	Day 115	Complete Lesson 12 Exercise 4 • Page 159			
Week 6	Day 116	Complete Lesson 12 Exercise 5 • Page 160			
	Day 117				
	Day 118	Review Course Assessment Chart; review lessons if student still needs to master the skill. Teacher aids are available in the back of the book.			
	Day 119				
	Day 120	Read Bible • Page 161 Complete Lesson 13 Exercise 1 • Page 162			

Date	Day	Assignment	Due Date	✓	Grade
	Day 121	Complete Lesson 13 Exercise 2 • Pages 163–165			
	Day 122				
Week 7	Day 123	Complete Lesson 13 Exercise 3 • Page 166			
	Day 124				
	Day 125	Begin Lesson 13 Exercise 4 • Pages 167–168			
	Day 126	Complete Lesson 13 Exercise 4 • Page 169			
	Day 127				
Week 8	Day 128	Complete Lesson 13 Exercise 5 • Page 170			
	Day 129				
	Day 130	Read Together • Page 171 Begin Lesson 14 Exercise 1 • Page 172			
	Day 131	Complete Lesson 14 Exercise 1 • Page 173			
	Day 132				
Week 9	Day 133	Complete Lesson 14 Exercise 2 • Pages 174–175			
	Day 134				
	Day 135	Complete Lesson 14 Exercise 3 • Pages 176–178			
Second Semester-Fourth Quarter					
	Day 136	Complete Lesson 14 Exercise 4 • Page 179			
	Day 137				
Week 1	Day 138	Complete Lesson 14 Exercise 5 • Page 180			
	Day 139				
	Day 140	Picture Study • Page 181 Complete Lesson 15 Exercise 1 • Pages 182–183			
	Day 141	Complete Lesson 15 Exercise 2 • Pages 184–187			
	Day 142				
Week 2	Day 143	Complete Lesson 15 Exercise 3 • Pages 188–190			
	Day 144				
	Day 145	Complete Lesson 15 Exercise 4 • Pages 191–193			
	Day 146	Complete Lesson 15 Exercise 5 • Page 194			
	Day 147				
Week 3	Day 148	Read Together • Page 195 Complete Lesson 16 Exercise 1 • Page 196			
	Day 149				
	Day 150	Begin Lesson 16 Exercise 2 • Pages 197–198			
	Day 151	Complete Lesson 16 Exercise 2 • Pages 199–201			
	Day 152				
Week 4	Day 153	Complete Lesson 16 Exercise 3 • Pages 202–204			
	Day 154				
	Day 155	Complete Lesson 16 Exercise 4 • Pages 205–207			

Date	Day	Assignment	Due Date	✓	Grade
Week 5	Day 156	Complete Lesson 16 Exercise 5 • Page 208			
	Day 157				
	Day 158	Review Course Assessment Chart; review lessons if student still needs to master the skill. Teacher aids are available in the back of the book.			
	Day 159				
	Day 160	Read Poem • Page 209 Complete Lesson 17 Exercise 1 • Pages 210–211			
Week 6	Day 161	Complete Lesson 17 Exercise 2 • Pages 212–214			
	Day 162				
	Day 163	Complete Lesson 17 Exercise 3 • Pages 215–217			
	Day 164				
	Day 165	Complete Lesson 17 Exercise 4 • Pages 218–219			
Week 7	Day 166	Complete Lesson 17 Exercise 5 • Page 220			
	Day 167				
	Day 168	Read Together • Page 221 Complete Lesson 18 Exercise 1 • Page 221			
	Day 169				
	Day 170	Complete Lesson 18 Exercise 2 • Pages 222–224			
Week 8	Day 171	Complete Lesson 18 Exercise 3 • Pages 225–227			
	Day 172				
	Day 173	Complete Lesson 18 Exercise 4 • Pages 228–229			
	Day 174				
	Day 175	Have the student read *The Door of Salvation* to the teacher (See teacher note on page 229)			
Week 9	Day 176	Complete Lesson 18 Exercise 5 • Page 230			
	Day 177				
	Day 178	Review Course Assessment Chart; review lessons if student still needs to master the skill. Teacher aids are available in the back of the book.			
	Day 179				
	Day 180	Present Certificate of Completion to the student!			
		Final Grade			

 **READING TOGETHER**

We are going to read a special book together called *Not Too Small at All*. The first time we read this book, I will read it to you. We will read through the story again a little at a time each week. As we read it again, you will get a chance to read part of the story. It is going to be fun! Are you ready?

 **TEACHER NOTE**
- Read *Not Too Small at All* to the student.

 **ORAL NARRATION PRACTICE**

Can you tell the story back to me? This is called narration. I can ask you some questions to help you remember.

 **TEACHER NOTE**
- If the student needs help, ask the following questions and allow him or her to answer them. You may also ask additional questions if needed.

(1) How does the story begin?

(2) Back when he was young, what did Grandpa Mouse decide to do? What happened?

(3) What did the bird tell Grandpa Mouse?

(4) Where did Grandpa Mouse go after that? What happened? How does the story end?

Now let's look at the cover of the book. The full title is *Not Too Small at All, a Mouse Tale*. The author is Stephanie Z. Townsend. She wrote the book! The illustrator is Bill Looney. An illustrator is the person who drew the pictures. Bill Looney created all the pictures in this book!

Let's open our book to page 4. I am going to read part of the page; then you are going to read part of it. We are going to read a page together!

TEACHER NOTE

- Show the student the title, author, and illustrator on the cover of the book.
- Read the page with the student, pointing to each word as it is read, until Grandpa begins to speak.
- Allow the student to read, starting with "Once upon a time. . . ." The student may also read the sentence here if he or she needs help with phonetic markings. You may want to review the phonetic sounds in the back of the book. Tell the student that a letter that is grey means it is silent. Example: līke
- Help the student sound out words if he or she has difficulty. Give cues, especially with vowel sounds. Remind the student (if needed) that in most words, the silent-e at the end makes the vowel say its name.

Now it is your turn to read!

"Once upŏn a tīme, long, long agō whĕn Ⓘ was ā yoŭng mouse līke yoū . . ."

REVIEW SIGHT WORDS

Let's look at some words. Which ones can you read to me?

TEACHER NOTE
- Circle any words the student cannot read quickly or struggles with.
- Create flashcards for all the circled words. They will be reviewed at the beginning of each week until the student can read them quickly.

and	an	as	at
in	is	it	if
did	of	on	not
a	I	be	see
all	but	to	for
from	or	so	no
are	he	was	his
how	can	we	had
will	has	get	the

that	this	than	when
what	who	then	them
they	out	she	have
you	by	my	belong

Great job! You are getting good at reading!

 **INDEPENDENT READING**

 **TEACHER NOTE**
- The student should practice reading simple books, starting with a few words and building up to a sentence and then multiple sentences per page. A reminder is given at the start of each week, but the student should read out loud to the teacher daily. We recommend using this reminder to select books for the week. They may be written down in the Book Reading List in the back of the book.

PHONICS NEW & REVIEW

Let's review the sounds some letter combinations make. First, I am going to say the letters; then I am going to make the sound the letters make together. Next, I will read a word that has the sound; then you will read a word that has the sound. Are you ready?

TEACHER NOTE

- Most of the letters/sounds were covered in *Foundations Phonics*. If the student hasn't learned the sounds, please take time to practice with him or her. New letters/sounds covered in this lesson are indicated with an asterisk (*).
- Read the chart like this: "The letters *s-p* sound like /sp/ like the word *spout*." Then allow the student to read the word shown.
- Name the pictures before the student writes in the correct letters.

Letters	Sounds Like	As In	Read
sp	/sp/	spout	spĭn
*tw	/tw/	twin	twĭg

Let's study some letter combinations that have a silent letter. The second letter in each of these letter combinations stays silent.

Letters	Sounds Like	As In	Read
wh	/w/	whale	whĭp
*mb	/m/	comb	lămb

Let's study some letter combinations that are usually found at the end of a word.

Letters	Sounds Like	As In	Read
ck	/ck/	sick	dŭck
ng	/ng/	wing	sŏng
*nk	/nk/	wink	sĭnk

Write the missing letters for each word.

1. _____in

2. _____ig

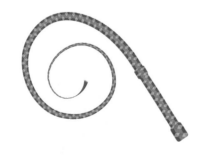

3. _____ip

4. la_____

5. **du**_____

6. **so**_____

7. **si**_____

 Sometimes a word doesn't follow the rules! There is a word in your sight words that starts with *wh*, but it makes a sound closer to the /h/ sound. Can you think of it? It is the word *who*.

TEACHER NOTE • The ⚠ means the sound is an exception to the rule.

 **LET'S SING**

Let's review the alphabet by singing the Alphabet Song.

TEACHER NOTE • Sing the Alphabet Song with the student.

LET'S WRITE

Write the alphabet in upper case.

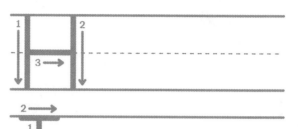

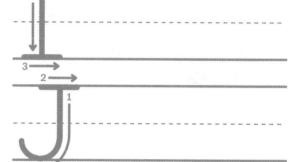

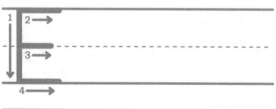

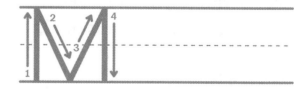

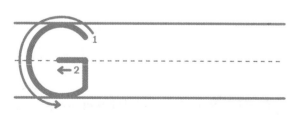

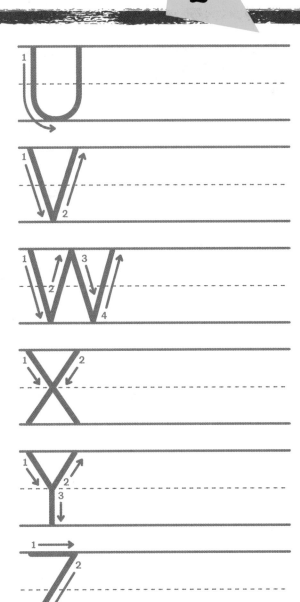

 **LET'S REVIEW AND APPLY**

Do you know the names of the vowels? The vowels are:

a   e   i   o   u

Most vowels are found in the middle of words. All the other letters are called consonants.

Let's memorize the vowels!

TEACHER NOTE
- Work with student until the vowels have been memorized.
- For practice, you can sing "Old MacDonald had a vowel...A, E, I, O, U."

Now that we have memorized the vowels, let's write them.

Great job!

Letters in words sometimes follow rules. Let's learn one of the rules they follow. Are you ready? Listen carefully. Here is the rule:

> The silent-e at the end of the word makes the vowel say its name. We call this the long vowel sound.

Let's study a word that has a silent-e at the end of the word. Notice that we show the silent-e in grey.

cage

Notice the silent-e at the end of this word. What sound does the *a* make in this word?

Yes, it makes the /a/ sound. Now read the word. Good job!

What does the silent-e at the end of a word do?

Yes! It makes the vowel say its name! This is the long vowel sound.

Let's look on page 4 of *Not Too Small at All.*

Can you show me some vowels on the page?

Can you show me some consonants?

Can you find a word where the silent-e makes the vowel say its name?

 **PHONICS FUN!**

What are the vowels?

Good job!

Do you remember what the letters are called that aren't vowels?

Yes, they are consonants!

Write the correct consonant at the beginning of each word.

1. _____all

2. _____an

3. _____at

4. _____um

5. _____og

6. _____at

7. ___ar

8. ___en

9. ___ey

10. ___oll

11. ___ip

12. ___un

 **CREATE YOUR OWN DICTIONARY!**

You are going to create your very own dictionary! A dictionary is a book of words. It shows how a word is spelled and what it means.

Let's read the words you are going to put in your dictionary.

 **TEACHER NOTE**
- Help the student read the words below.

- Dictionary pages are found in the back of the book. Copies may be made if the student wants to add his or her own words to the dictionary. The student may want to keep his or her dictionary in a binder.

- The student will be exposed to new phonics sounds with his or her dictionary words. Discuss the new sounds with the student as they come up.

chair   cookie   door

happy   house   mouse

Let's put our first word in the dictionary.

 **TEACHER NOTE**
- You will find instructions on page 264 in this book for how the dictionary pages should be used. It will also have a helpful example using the word *happy* from this lesson.

 **PICTURE STUDY**

Let's take some time to study this picture.

 **OBSERVATION SKILLS**

 **TEACHER NOTE** • Questions should be read by the teacher and answered orally by the student.

(1) What is happening in this picture that is told about in the Bible?

(2) What kind of animal is shown?

(3) What colors are used?

(4) What does the sky look like?

(5) What does the land look like?

(6) How does the picture make you feel?

READING TOGETHER

Do you remember the first part of the story of *Not Too Small at All*? Narrate, or tell it, to me.

Let's read *Not Too Small at All* together. I will read page 6 to you.

Now it is your turn to read! Let's look at page 7. You get to read the first sentence!

TEACHER NOTE

- Review previous pages if student doesn't remember.
- Read new pages to the student.
- Student may read from the book or below.
- After the student reads, finish reading the page to the student, pointing to each word as it is read.
- Help the student sound out words as needed. Give clues, especially with vowel sounds.

Whĕn I was yŏung, I lĭved alōne ĭn a smȧll hōle ĭn a house ĭn the cĭty.

What happened in today's section of the story? Can you tell it back to me?

REVIEW SIGHT WORDS

Review sight words using the flashcards created for words the student is still learning.

INDEPENDENT READING

PHONICS NEW & REVIEW

Let's review the sounds some letter combinations make. First, I am going to say the letters; then I am going to make the sound the letters make together. Next, I will read a word that has the sound; then you will read a word that has the sound. Are you ready?

TEACHER NOTE

• Most of the letters/ sounds were covered in *Foundations Phonics*. If the student hasn't learned the sounds, please take time to practice with him or her. New letters/sounds covered in this lesson are indicated with an asterisk (*).

Next, we are going to study letters that make a whole new sound when they are together!

Letters	Sounds Like	As In	Read
sh	/sh/	ship	shŏp
ch	/ch/	child	chĭp
qu	/qu/	quilt	quĭz
*ph	/f/	phone	phōtō

Write the missing letters for each word.

1. _____op

2. _____ip

3. _____iz

4. _____oto

Sometimes words have double letters. We only say the letter sound once in many words that have double letters. Let's study some examples.

Letters	Sounds Like	As In	Read
*dd	/d/	add	ŏdd
*ff	/f/	puff	cŭff
*ll	/l/	llama	båll

* ss	/s/	kiss	měss
* tt	/t/	mitt	mŭtt
* zz	/z/	fizz	bŭzz

Write the missing letters for each word.

1, 3, 5, 7, 9

_____

5. o_____

6. cu_____

_____

7. ba_____

8. me_____

_____   _____

9. mu_____   10. bu_____

 **LET'S SING**   Let's review the alphabet by singing the Alphabet Song.

 **LET'S WRITE**   Write the alphabet in lower case.

a   f

b   g

c   h

d   i

e   j

k

s

l

t

m

u

n

v

o

w

p

x

q

y

r

z

 LET'S REVIEW
AND APPLY

What are the vowels?

 TEACHER NOTE
- See if student can remember the vowels and their different sounds.
- Point to each spelled word as you read it. The student may also read it.
- If the student needs extra help, say a word with the sound in it. Spend time reviewing vowel sounds if needed.

a   e   i   o   u

Do you remember the 3 sounds the letter *a* can make?

The letter *a* can make the short-a sound as in:	It can make the long-a sound as in:	It can make the *å* sound as in:
măp	lāke	båll

Do you remember the 2 sounds the letter *e* can make?

The letter *e* can make the short-e sound as in:	The letter *e* can make the long-e sound as in:
bĕd	wē

Do you remember the 2 sounds the letter *i* can make?

The letter *i* can make the short-i sound as in:	The letter *i* can make the long-i sound as in:
sĭt	pīe

Do you remember the 2 sounds the letter *o* can make?

The letter *o* can make	The letter *o* can make
the short-o as in:	the long-o as in:
pŏp	grōw

Do you remember the 2 sounds the letter *u* can make?

The letter *u* can make	The letter *u* can make
the short-u as in:	the long-u as in:
bŭs	cūbe

PICTURE STUDY

Let's look at the pictures on pages 6–7 of *Not Too Small at All.*

(1) Whose hand is poking through the mouse hole?

(2) What is the finger pushing?

(3) What are the mice using for a blanket and bed?

(4) What kind of trees are in the picture?

(5) How is the house in the picture different from the house you live in?

(6) What is your favorite thing about the pictures?

 **PHONICS FUN!**

Do you remember what the letters are called that are not vowels?

Yes, they are consonants!

Write the correct consonant at the beginning of each word.

1. ___an

2. ___uilt

3. ___ut

4. ___ug

5. ___an

6. ___ad

7. ___ub

8. ___ox

9. ___an

10. ___ak

11. ___eb

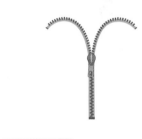

12. ___ip

 **CREATE YOUR OWN DICTIONARY!**

 **TEACHER NOTE**   • Help the student read the words below.

Let's read the words you can put in your dictionary today.

birds

dinosaur

dog

plow

seeds

sheep

Remember, for each word you will:

- Find the page that has the same letter your word starts with.
- Write the word on the top line.
- Draw a picture that shows what the word means.
- Write a simple definition (or meaning) for the word.

READING TOGETHER

Do you remember what happened up to now in the story of *Not Too Small at All*? Narrate, or tell it, to me.

Let's read *Not Too Small at All* together. I will read page 8 to you. You get to read the last sentence!

Now it is your turn to read!

TEACHER NOTE

- Review pages 4–7 if needed.

- Read page 8 to the student, stopping before the last sentence. Be sure to point to each word as you read.

- Help the student sound out words as needed. Cover up part of a large word while the student sounds it out, such as "everyone." Encourage him or her to sound out larger words. They are just like small words, only they take more time to get through. Have patience as the student sounds out the words. Tell the student the word (showing how it is sounded out) and move on if there is sign of frustration.

- Have the student break the word "everyone" into two words, "every" and "one." Help the student read the word "important" by focusing on each syllable at a time. Also, be sure to point out how the letters *or* blend together to say /or/. If the student shows any sign of frustration, model how to sound out the word, read it to the student, then move on and allow the student to read the next word in the sentence.

Ĕvĕryone hăd a very ĭmpōrtănt jŏb to do.

Now let's read page 9 of our story.

What happened in today's part of the story? Can you tell it back to me?

REVIEW SIGHT WORDS

Review sight words using the flashcards created for words the student is still learning.

INDEPENDENT READING

JUST 4 FUN!

Connect the dots to reveal the shape! What is it? Write the word on the line below. You may color the picture.

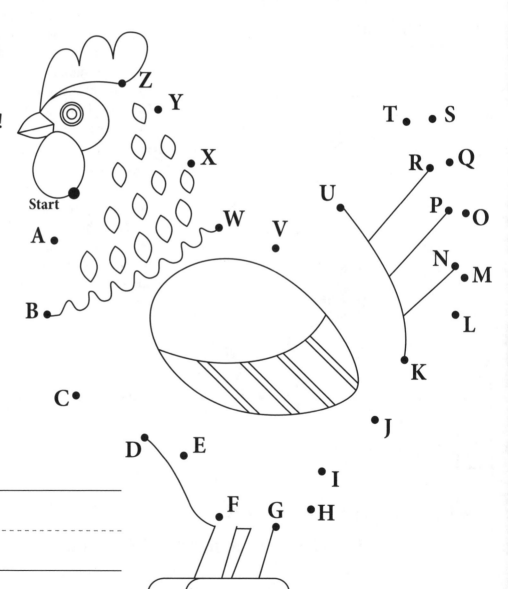

_____

- -

_____

 **PHONICS NEW & REVIEW**

 **TEACHER NOTE**
- Some of the letters/sounds were covered in *Foundations Phonics*. If the student hasn't learned the sounds, please take time to practice with him or her. New letters/sounds covered in this lesson are indicated with an asterisk (*).
- Repeat the words *with* and *those* until the student can hear the slightly different sounds of *th*.

Let's review the sounds some letter combinations make. First, I am going to say the letters; then I am going to make the sound the letters make together. Next, I will read a word that has the sound; then you will read a word that has the sound.

Let's listen to the two slightly different sounds *th* can make. Listen carefully.

The letters *th* can make the /th/ sound as in the word *those*.

The letters *th* can make the /th/ sound as in the word *with*.

Do you hear the different sounds *th* can make?

Letters	Sounds Like	As In	Read
th	/th/	this	thăt
*th	/th/	thanks	thĭnk

Write the missing letters for each word.

1. _____at

2. _____ink

Let's study some new letter combinations. The first letter in each letter combination stays silent.

Letters	Sounds Like	As In	Read
* kn	/n/	knit	knŏt
* lf	/f/	calf	hălf
* lk	/k/	walk	tålk

The letter *y* sometimes acts like a consonant and sometimes like a vowel.

Letters	Sounds Like	As In	Read
y	/y/	yak	yĕs
y	/ī/	sky	spy
* y	/ē/	lady	bāby

Write the missing letters for the word.

_____

_____

3. _____ot

4. ha_____

_____

_____

5. ta_____

6. __es

_____

_____

7. sp____

8. bab____

LET'S SING

Let's review the alphabet by singing the Alphabet Song.

LET'S WRITE

Write the **uppercase** letter that goes with the lowercase letter.

a

b

c

d

e

f

g

h

i

j

k

l

m _____   t _____

n _____   u _____

o _____   v _____

p _____   w _____

q _____   x _____

r _____   y _____

s _____   z _____

 **LET'S REVIEW AND APPLY**

What are the vowels? Write them.

 **TEACHER NOTE**

- See if student can remember the vowels and their sounds. Remind him or her if needed.
- If the student needs extra help, say a word with the sound in it. Spend time reviewing vowel sounds if needed.
- Point to each word and have the student read it.

_____

- -

_____

Let's see if you remember what sounds the vowels make.

Do you remember the 3 sounds the letter *a* can make? Let's read words with the letter *a*:

| măp | lāke | båll |

Copy the letter *a* words:

map _____

lake _____

ball _____

Do you remember the 2 sounds the letter *e* can make?

Let's read words with the letter *e*:

bĕd   wē

Copy the words that show the 2 sounds the letter *e* can make:

bed _____

_____

we _____

Do you remember the 2 sounds the letter *i* can make?

Let's read words with the letter *i*:

sĭt   pīe

Copy the words that show the 2 sounds the letter *i* can make:

sit _____

_____

pie _____

Do you remember the 2 sounds the letter *o* can make?

Let's read words with the letter *o*:

pŏp   hōle

Copy the words that show the 2 sounds the letter *o* can make:

pop

_____

_____

_____

hole

_____

Do you remember the 2 sounds the letter *u* can make?

Let's read words with the letter *u*:

bŭs   cūbe

Copy the words that show the 2 sounds the letter *u* can make:

bus

_____

_____

cube

_____

Name_____

 **PICTURE STUDY**

Let's look at the pictures on pages 8–9 of *Not Too Small at All*. The clouds above the head of the mouse show what he is thinking about.

(1) What is happening in the picture on page 9?

(2) What is the mouse holding in his hand on page 9?

(3) What is wrapped around the dog's neck on page 9? What color is it?

(4) What is your favorite part of the pictures?

 **PHONICS FUN!**   Today we are going to work with vowels. You should know them by now! They are *a-e-i-o-u*.

Sometimes letters are tricky and break the rules! Let's learn about one of these rule breakers!

We learned the letter *u* can make two sounds: *u* as in *bus* and *u* as in *cube*.

Sometimes the letter *u* makes the /oo/ sound as in *tube*!

Let's read three words that have the letter *u*. Can you hear the different sounds the *u* makes in these words?

bŭs | cūbe | tube

Write the correct vowel in the middle of each word.

1. p___n   2. t___pe

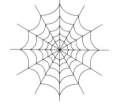

3. c___r   4. w___b

5. k___y

6. p___n

7. ___ce

8. ph___ne

9. f___x

10. s___n

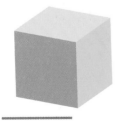

11. c___be

12. t___be

CREATE YOUR OWN DICTIONARY!

TEACHER NOTE • Help the student read the words below.

Let's read the words you can put in your dictionary today.

field   nest   oxen

pasture   run   trees

Remember, for each word you will:

- Find the page that has the same letter your word starts with.
- Write the word on the top line if empty or one of the other lines.
- Draw a picture that shows what the word means.
- Write a simple definition (or meaning) for the word.

 **LET'S READ THE BIBLE**

Matthew 19 verses 13–15 tells us about how Jesus blessed children. Let's read about it.

 **TEACHER NOTE** • You may use your own translation rather than NASB.

¹³Then some children were brought to Him so that He might lay His hands on them and pray; and the disciples rebuked them.

¹⁴But Jesus said, "Let the children alone, and do not hinder them from coming to Me; for the kingdom of heaven belongs to such as these."

¹⁵After laying His hands on them, He departed from there.

 **ORAL NARRATION PRACTICE**

 **TEACHER NOTE** • Allow the student to answer but take time to discuss the passage.

Let's think about what we read.

(1) Why were the children brought to Jesus?

(2) The passage doesn't tell us, but who do you think brought the children to Jesus?

(3) What did the disciples do?

(4) Why do you think the disciples did that?

(5) What did Jesus say to the disciples?

(6) What did Jesus do before He left?

(7) Based on this passage, how do you think Jesus feels about children?

(8) How do you think Jesus feels about you?

 **READING TOGETHER**

Do you remember what happened up to now in the story of *Not Too Small at All*? Narrate, or tell it, to me.

 **TEACHER NOTE**
- Review pages 4–9 if needed.
- Read page 10 to the student, stopping before the last sentence. Be sure to point to each word as you read.
- Help the student sound out words if he or she has difficulty. Cover up part of a large word while the student sounds it out. Encourage him or her to sound out larger words. Have patience as the student sounds out the words. Tell him or her the word (showing how it is sounded out) and move on if there is sign of frustration.
- Student may read from the book or below.

Let's read page 10 of *Not Too Small at All*. I will read until the last sentence; then you get to read!

Now it is your turn to read!

My squēak was mŭch too sŏft, and whĕn I trīed to bīte thĕm, they jŭst stĕpped on my hĕad and my tāil.

Now let's read page 11 of our story.

What happened in today's part of the story? Can you tell it back to me?

 **REVIEW SIGHT WORDS**   Review sight words using the flashcards created for words the student is still learning.

 **INDEPENDENT READING**

PHONICS NEW & REVIEW

Let's review the sounds some letter combinations make. First, I am going to say the letters; then I am going to make the sound the letters make together. Next, I will read a word that has the sound; then you will read a word that has the sound. Are you ready?

TEACHER NOTE

• Some of the letters/sounds were covered in *Foundations Phonics*. If the student hasn't learned the sounds, please take time to practice with him or her. New letters/sounds covered in this lesson are indicated with an asterisk (*).

Letters	Sounds Like	As In	Read
ea	/ĕ/	bread	hĕad
*ea	/ē/	beam	sēat

Write the missing letters for each word.

1. h_____d

2. s_____t

LET'S SING

Let's review the alphabet by singing the Alphabet Song.

LET'S WRITE

Write the **lowercase** alphabet letter that goes with the uppercase letter.

A

B

C

D

E

F

G

H

I

J

K

L

M

N

O

P

Q

R

S

T

U

V

W

X

Y

Z

LET'S REVIEW AND APPLY

What are the vowels?

Let's see if you remember what sounds the vowels make.

Do you remember the 3 sounds *a* makes?

Do you remember the 2 sounds *e* makes?

Do you remember the 2 sounds *i* makes?

Do you remember the 2 sounds *o* makes?

Do you remember the 2 sounds *u* makes?

TEACHER NOTE

- If the student needs extra help, say a word with the sound in it. Spend time reviewing vowel sounds if needed.
- The vowels make the following sounds:
- short-a as in *map*, long-a as in *lake*, the third *a* sound as in *ball*
- short-e as in *bed*, long-e as in *we*
- short-i as in *sit*, long-i as in *pie*
- short-o as in *pop*, long-o as in *hole*
- short-u as in *bus*, long-u as in *use*

PICTURE STUDY

Let's look at the pictures on pages 10–11 of *Not Too Small at All*.

(1) Why are the dogs laughing on page 10?

(2) What do you think the mouse is thinking on page 10?

(3) If cows could talk, what do you think they would say on page 11?

(4) How do you think the mouse feels on page 11?

(5) What is your favorite thing about the pictures?

 **PHONICS FUN!**

Today we are going to work with vowels. You should know them by now! They are *a-e-i-o-u*.

Circle the correct vowel sound found in the middle of each word.

1. ā ī ū

2. ĕ ŏ ă

3. ā ē ō

4. å ŭ ĭ

5. ŭ ŏ ă

6. ĕ ŏ ă

7. ŭ   ĕ   ă

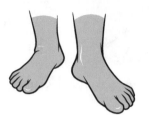

8. ē   ū   ō

9. ŭ   ĕ   ă

10. ē   ū   ō

11. å   ŏ   ă

12. ŭ   ŏ   ă

JUST **4** FUN!

Find and circle three differences
between the pictures.

 **CREATE YOUR OWN DICTIONARY!**

TEACHER NOTE • Help the student read the words below.

Let's read the words you can put in your dictionary today.

fence

moon

mud

orchard

sun

wings

Remember, for each word you will:

- Find the page that has the same letter your word starts with.
- Write the word on the top line if empty or one of the other lines.
- Draw a picture that shows what the word means.
- Write a simple definition (or meaning) for the word.

READING TOGETHER

Do you remember what happened up to now in the story of *Not Too Small at All*? Narrate, or tell it, to me.

Let's read page 12 of *Not Too Small at All*.

Now let's read page 13 of *Not Too Small at All*. You are going to read the first sentence.

TEACHER NOTE

- Review pages 4–11 if needed.

- Read page 12 to the student. Be sure to point to each word as you read.

- Help the student sound out words if he or she has difficulty. Cover up part of a large word while the student sounds it out. Encourage him or her to sound out larger words. Have patience as the student sounds out the words. Tell him or her the word (showing how it is sounded out) and move on if there is sign of frustration.

- Student may read from the book or below.

The kīnd bird flew down to the grăssy spŏt where I lāy and lăndĕd sŏftly bēsīde mē.

What happened in today's part of the story?
Can you tell it back to me?

Exercise 1 Day 21

REVIEW SIGHT WORDS

Review sight words using the flashcards created for words the student is still learning.

INDEPENDENT READING

PHONICS NEW & REVIEW

Let's review words that use the letter combinations we have learned. Read each word as I point to it.

duck	song	sink
spin	whip	lamb
twig	shop	chip
quiz	photo	odd
cuff	ball	mess
mutt	buzz	that
think	knot	half
talk	head	seat

Let's study some new letter combinations.

The letters *gh* can make three different sounds!

It can sound like /f/ as in the word *tough*.

It can stay silent as in the word *night*.

Not very often, it makes the /g/ sound as in the word *gherkin*. (That is a type of pickle!)

Letters	Sounds Like	As In	Read
gh	/g/	aghast	ghōst
gh	/f/	rough	lăugh
gh	silent	dough	hīgh

Write the missing letters for each word.

1. tou_____

2. hi_____

3. _____erkin

 **LET'S WRITE**

Let's write words. Copy the words on the lines.

bad

cat

men

yes

dip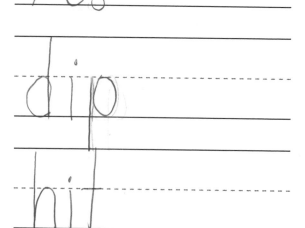

hit

dog   dog

owl   owl

bud   bud

run   run

You did it!

LET'S REVIEW AND APPLY

Let's review the words you wrote in the last lesson. Read them to me.

bad	cat	men	yes
dip	hit	dog	owl
bud	run		

Do the words have short or long vowel sounds?

Let's read the words again, but this time spell the word after you read it.

Now I am going to read each word to you. Let's see if you can remember how to spell it. It will be fun!

TEACHER NOTE

• The student should read the word then spell it. Example: can c-a-n

• Read each word to the student. The student should spell the word, out loud, without looking. Go back and study the words until he or she can spell them from memory.

• The student may also write each word on an index card to practice. The student may create right-brain flashcards by drawing pictures on the cards or around the letters to help him or her remember how to spell the words.

PICTURE STUDY

Look at the pictures on pages 12–13 of *Not Too Small at All*.

(1) Tell the story of what happened to the mouse as told on page 12. Use the pictures to remind you of what happened.

(2) How do you think the mouse feels in the picture on page 13?

(3) Have you ever felt like that?

(4) What do you think the bird wants to say to the mouse?

(5) What would you say to the mouse if you were the bird?

(6) What is your favorite thing about the pictures on these two pages?

JUST 4 FUN!   Help the mouse get the grass to the nest.

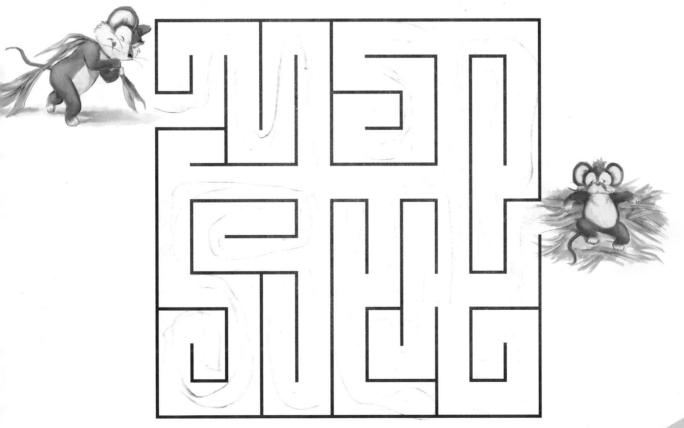

Spelling Fun!

Today we are going to spell words. There is a picture of each word we studied. Write the correct word under the picture.

TEACHER NOTE

• The words in this lesson are found on pages 76–77. The student may study them before completing this page.

1. _____

2. _____

3. _____

4. _____

5. _____

6. _____

7. _____

8. _____

9. _____

10. _____

Word Fun!

Did you know that there are different kinds of words? Some words are things. I can think of a few words that are things. How about *shirt*? A shirt is a thing. How about *book*? A book is a thing.

TEACHER NOTE
- Let the student name some nouns. Practice naming nouns if he or she has trouble identifying things as nouns.

Words that are things are called nouns.

Can you think of any nouns?

Good job!

11. Circle the pictures that show a noun.

   Hint: Don't circle the actions; circle the things.

 **TEACHER NOTE**

- For clarification, we have included the words below the images to help the student focus on the concept of a noun or verb instead of just what is in the picture. Please read the word below each image for the student to help him or her understand the concept.

brush

run

cat

frog

doll

zip

dog

toy

hit

How many squares do you see?

 **CREATE YOUR OWN DICTIONARY!**

 **TEACHER NOTE** • Help the student read the words below.

Let's read the words you can put in your dictionary today.

bed   hills   stars

wake   yawn   zoo

Remember, for each word you will:

• Find the page that has the same letter your word starts with.

• Write the word on the top line if empty or one of the other lines.

• Draw a picture that shows what the word means.

• Write a simple definition (or meaning) for the word.

PICTURE STUDY

Title: *Young Mother Sewing*, 1900
Artist: Mary Cassatt

Do you remember when we looked at the cover of our book and saw who wrote it and who created the pictures? The artist of this painting is Mary Cassatt. She painted it. Let's study this picture for a few minutes. The title is what people call the painting. It is called *Young Mother Sewing*. Mary Cassatt painted it in the year 1900. That was a long time ago, but people still enjoy looking at her painting today.

OBSERVATION SKILLS

(1) What do you like about this painting?

(2) Where does this painting take place?

(3) What colors are used?

(4) What is happening in the painting?

(5) What do you see in this painting? Name as many things as you can!

READING TOGETHER

Do you remember what happened up to now in the story of *Not Too Small at All*? Narrate, or tell it, to me.

Let's read page 14 of *Not Too Small at All*.

Now let's read page 15 of *Not Too Small at All*. You are going to read the first sentence.

TEACHER NOTE

- Review pages 4–13 if needed.

- Read page 14 to the student. Be sure to point to each word as you read.

- Help the student sound out words if he or she has difficulty. Cover up part of a large word while the student sounds it out. Encourage him or her to sound out larger words. Have patience as the student sounds out the words. Tell him or her the word (showing how it is sounded out) and move on if there is sign of frustration.

- Student may read from the book or below.

The nĕxt mōrnĭng I wōke as the sŭn cāme pēekĭng up from bēhīnd the hĭlls jŭst līke ĕvery other dāy, ōnly thĭs was no ōrdĭnāry dāy.

What happened in today's part of the story?
Can you tell it back to me?

REVIEW SIGHT WORDS

Review sight words using the flashcards created for words the student is still learning.

INDEPENDENT READING

PHONICS NEW & REVIEW

Let's review words that use the letter combinations we have learned. Read each word as I point to it.

pick	wing	sink
spout	whale	comb
twin	ship	child
quilt	phone	add
puff	llama	kiss
mitt	fizz	this
thanks	knit	calf
walk	bread	beam

Let's study some new letter combinations. Let's look at what happens when we add a consonant before the letter *l*.

Letters	Sounds Like	As In	Read
bl	/bl/	block	blŭsh
cl	/cl/	clock	clăp
fl	/fl/	flock	flăg
gl	/gl/	globe	glăd
pl	/pl/	plant	plŭm
sl	/sl/	slide	slĕd

Write the missing letters for each word.

1. _____ush   2. _____ap

_____

- - - - - - - - - -

3. _____ag

_____

- - - - - - - - - -

4. _____ad

_____

- - - - - - - - - -

5. _____um

_____

- - - - - - - - - -

6. _____ed

We can do this!

 **LET'S WRITE**

 **TEACHER NOTE** • Save these two pages for the student to study for a future lesson.

We can change a short vowel to a long vowel by adding a silent-e to the word. The silent-e makes a vowel say its name.

Let's change 3-letter words into new words by adding a silent-e to the end of the word.

Copy the first word, then add the silent-e at the end.

7. can

8. bit

_____

- -

9. pin   _____

_____

- -

10. not   _____

_____

- -

11. cut   _____

 **LET'S REVIEW AND APPLY**

Let's review the words you wrote in the last lesson. Read them to me.

can	cane	bit	bite
pin	pine	not	note
cut	cute		

Which words make the short vowel sound — the first words you read or the words you added an *e* to?

Which words make a long vowel sound?

What sound does the *e* you added to the end of each word make? Remember, the silent-e at the end of a word makes the vowel say its name.

Read the words to me.

Let's read the words again, but this time spell the word after you read it.

Now I am going to read each word to you. Let's see if you can remember how to spell it. It will be fun!

 **TEACHER NOTE**

- The student should read the word then spell it. Example: can c-a-n

- Read each word to the student. The student should spell the word, out loud, without looking. Go back and study the words until he or she can spell them from memory.

- The student may also write each word on an index card to practice. The student may create right-brain flashcards by drawing pictures on the cards or around the letters to help him or her remember how to spell the words.

 PICTURE STUDY

Look at the pictures on pages 14–15 of *Not Too Small at All*.

(1) Describe what is happening in the pictures on page 14.

(2) Who is holding the mouse?

(3) Where is the mouse on page 15?

(4) What is the mouse doing?

(5) What do you think the people are talking about?

(6) What is your favorite thing about the pictures on these two pages?

 JUST **4** FUN!   Find the two owls that are the same.

Spelling Fun!

Today we are going to spell words. There is a picture of each word we studied. Write the correct word under the picture.

1. _____

2. _____

3. _____

4. _____

5. _____

6. _____

_____   _____

- - - - - - - - - - - - - -   - - - - - - - - - - - - - -

7. _____   8. _____

_____   _____

- - - - - - - - - - - - - -   - - - - - - - - - - - - - -

9. _____   10. _____

Word Fun!

Do you remember what a noun is? A noun is a thing. A noun can also be a person. You are a person. That means you are a noun! Your mom is a noun, and so is your dad! A noun that is a person can be a general name for a person like *brother* or *sister*. It also can describe what they do for their job like *doctor* or *writer*. It can also be a person's name like *Gideon* or *Ella*. When we write a person's name, we use a capital letter for the first letter.

Can you think of any other people nouns?

Good job!

TEACHER NOTE
• Let the student name some nouns that name people. Practice people nouns if he or she has trouble identifying them.

11. Circle the pictures that show a noun.

Remember, do not circle the actions, circle the things.

man

cut

friend

blow

cooking

maid

clap

boat

fruit

 **CREATE YOUR OWN DICTIONARY!**

 **TEACHER NOTE** • Help the student read the words below.

Let's read the words you can put in your dictionary today.

Ark

breakfast

eat

laugh

Noah

valley

Remember, for each word you will:

- Find the page that has the same letter your word starts with.
- Write the word on the top line if empty or one of the other lines.
- Draw a picture that shows what the word means.
- Write a simple definition (or meaning) for the word.

Help the mice find the ark.

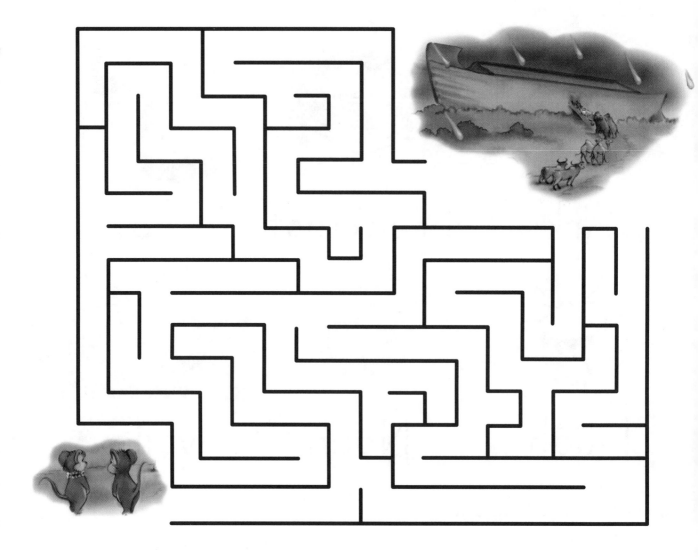

READING TOGETHER

Do you remember what happened up to now in the story of *Not Too Small at All*? Narrate, or tell it, to me.

Let's read page 16. You are going to read the first sentence.

TEACHER NOTE
• Review pages 4–15 if needed.

• Read page 16 to the student. Be sure to point to each word as you read.

• Help the student sound out words if he or she has difficulty. Cover up part of a large word while the student sounds it out. Encourage him or her to sound out larger words. Have patience as the student sounds out the words. Tell him or her the word (showing how it is sounded out) and move on if there is sign of frustration.

• Student may read from the book or below.

From the tīme I was a very yŏung mouse, I had avoidĕd that văllēy whenĕver pŏssĭble.

Did you notice the silent-e in the word *time*?

What happened in today's part of the story?
Can you tell it back to me?

Exercise 1 **Day 31**

REVIEW SIGHT WORDS

INDEPENDENT READING

Review sight words using the flashcards created for words the student is still learning.

**PHONICS
NEW & REVIEW**

Let's review words that use the letter combinations we have learned. Read each word as I point to it.

duck	wing	wink
spin	whale	lamb
twig	shop	child
quilt	photo	odd
puff	ball	kiss
mutt	fizz	this
think	knot	calf
talk	head	beam

Let's study some new letter combinations. Let's look at what happens when we add a consonant before the letter *r*.

Letters	Sounds Like	As In	Read
br	/br/	brick	brŭsh
cr	/cr/	crate	crăb
dr	/dr/	dress	drŭm
fr	/fr/	fruit	frŏg
gr	/gr/	grape	grŭb
pr	/pr/	prize	prĕss
tr	/tr/	trick	trăsh
wr	/wr/	write	wrăp

Write the missing letters for each word.

1. _____ush

2. _____ab

3. _____um

4. _____og

5. _____ub

6. _____ess

7. _____ash

8. _____ap

**LET'S
WRITE**

**TEACHER
NOTE**
• Save this page and the
next for the student to
study for a future lesson.

We are going to work with words that include a silent letter and a long vowel.
Remember how a silent-e can make a vowel say its name? When we have a
vowel pair in the middle of a word, sometimes the second vowel is silent and
makes the first vowel say its name.

Look at the words below. Read each word out loud, then tell which vowel is
long and which vowel is silent.

Now, copy each word on the line next to it.

laid _____

maid _____

seat _____

meat

tied

lied

boat

coat

fruit

suit

LET'S REVIEW AND APPLY

Let's review the words you wrote in the last lesson.

laid	maid	seat	meat
tied	lied	boat	coat
fruit	suit		

Do you remember the two rules we learned about silent letters?

- The silent-e at the end of a word makes the vowel say its name.
  Examples: *tire care*

- When we have a vowel pair in the middle of a word, sometimes the second vowel is silent and makes the first vowel say its name.
  Examples: *team boat*

TEACHER NOTE

- The student should read the word then spell it. Example: can c-a-n

- Read each word to the student. The student should spell the word, out loud, without looking. Go back and study the words until he or she can spell them from memory.

- The student may also write each word on an index card to practice. The student may create right-brain flashcards by drawing pictures on the cards or around the letters to help him or her remember how to spell the words.

Let's read the words, but this time spell the word after you read it.

Now I am going to read each word to you. Let's see if you can remember how to spell it. It will be fun!

 **PICTURE STUDY**

Look at the pictures on pages 16–17 of *Not Too Small at All*.

(1) What is happening in the pictures on pages 16–17?

(2) Why does the mouse look so big compared to the people on page 16?

(3) Why do the people near the boat look so small on page 17?

(4) What do you think the two people closest to the mouse are talking about on page 16?

(5) What kinds of animals do you see?

(6) What is your favorite thing about this picture?

 **JUST 4 FUN!**

Both of the pictures below are words you have learned. Write them on the lines then complete the maze!

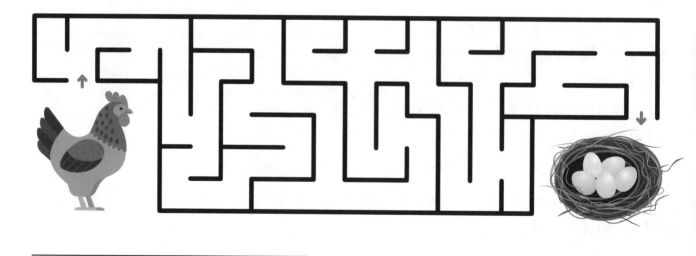

_____   _____
- - - - - - - - - - - - - - - - - -   - - - - - - - - - - - - - - - - - -
_____   _____

Spelling Fun!

Today we are going to spell words. There is a picture of each word we studied. Write the correct word under the picture.

1. _____

2. _____

3. _____

4. _____

5. _____

6. _____

7. _____ 8. _____

9. _____ 10. _____

Word Fun!

Do you remember what a noun is? We have learned that a noun can be a thing or a person. A noun can also be a place. A place could be the city, state, or country you live in! It could also be a place you like to go, like the store or a park. When we write the name of a city, state, or country, we use a capital letter for the first letter. Example: Ohio.

Can you think of any other place nouns?

Good job!

TEACHER NOTE
• Let the student name some nouns that name places. Practice place nouns if he or she has trouble identifying them.

11. Circle the pictures that show a noun.

Remember, do not circle the actions; circle the things. A noun can be a thing or a place.

planting

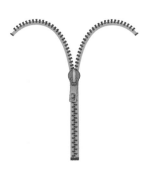

zip

lake

smile

zoo

canyon

bud

field

eat

 **CREATE YOUR OWN DICTIONARY!**

 **TEACHER NOTE**   • Help the student read the words below.

Let's read the words you can put in your dictionary today.

build   flood   grow

rain   under   wood

Remember, for each word you will:

- Find the page that has the same letter your word starts with.
- Write the word on the top line if empty or one of the other lines.
- Draw a picture that shows what the word means.
- Write a simple definition (or meaning) for the word.

 **LET'S READ A POEM**

I am going to read a poem to you.
Listen carefully as I read it.

"At the Sea-Side"
By Robert Louis Stevenson

When I was down beside the sea
A wooden spade they gave to me
To dig the sandy shore.

My holes were empty like a cup.
In every hole the sea came up,
Till it could come no more.

This poem is called "At the Sea-Side." It was written in the year 1913. That was a long time ago, but we can still enjoy it today.

Robert Louis Stevenson is the author of the poem. That means he wrote it.

Let's study this poem. This poem has words that rhyme. Two words that rhyme sound the same at the end of the word. In the first part of the poem, the words *sea* and *me* rhyme. Do you hear how they sound the same?

Let's circle the two words that rhyme in the first part of our poem.

I am going to read the second part of the poem to you. Can you tell me the words that rhyme?

Did you hear two words rhyme? What are they? Yes! The words *cup* and *up* rhyme. Let's circle them.

 **TEACHER NOTE**

- Read the first two lines to the student and emphasize the words *sea* and *me*.
- Read the second stanza of the poem and emphasize the words *cup* and *up*.
- Read the last line of each stanza, emphasizing the words *shore* and *more*.

(Source: Stevenson, R.L. (1913). *A Child's Garden of Verses*. Simon & Schuster Children's.)

This poem has two more words that rhyme! Let me read the last line of each part of the poem.

Did you hear two words rhyme? What are they? Yes! The words *shore* and *more* rhyme. Let's underline them.

I'm going to read the poem to you one more time.

 **ORAL NARRATION PRACTICE**

 **TEACHER NOTE**
- Allow the student to answer but take time to discuss the poem.

Let's think about what we read.

(1) What is the poem about?

(2) What do you think a wooden spade is?

(3) What happened to the holes?

(4) Would you have fun digging holes by the seaside?

 **READING TOGETHER**

 **TEACHER NOTE**
- Review pages 4–17 if needed.

Do you remember what happened up to now in the story of *Not Too Small at All*? Narrate, or tell it, to me.

Let's read page 18. You are going to read the first sentence.

- Read page 18 to the student. Be sure to point to each word as you read.

- Help the student sound out words if he or she has difficulty. Cover up part of a large word while the student sounds it out. Encourage him or her to sound out larger words. Have patience as the student sounds out the words. Tell him or her the word (showing how it is sounded out) and move on if there is sign of frustration.

- Student may read from the book or from the next page.

As I crĕpt down into the văllēy, I nōtĭced that many other ănĭmåls were gōĭng in the sāme dirĕction.

What happened in today's part of the story? Can you tell it back to me?

 **REVIEW SIGHT WORDS**

Review sight words using the flashcards created for words the student is still learning.

 **INDEPENDENT READING**

Great job!

PHONICS NEW & REVIEW

Let's review words that use the letter combinations we have learned. Read each word as I point to it.

ghost	laugh	high
blush	clap	flag
glad	plum	sled
brush	crab	drum
frog	grub	press
trash	wrap	

We are going to work with some tricky words. Some words don't like to follow the rules! We are going to read and write words that have the vowels *ie* in the middle. Some of them follow the rule that we learned about the second vowel making the first vowel say its name. We have to watch out, though, because some of these tricky *ie* vowels aren't following the rule!

Let's learn about these tricky *ie* vowels! In our words for today, the *ie* vowels make three different sounds!

TEACHER NOTE • Point to the example words below.

> The vowels *ie* can follow the rule and make the long-i sound. We see this in the words *pie* and *died*.

> The vowels *ie* can trade with each other! Instead of the second vowel being silent and the first vowel saying its name, the FIRST vowel is silent, and the SECOND vowel says its name. That means the *i* stays silent and the *e* says its name! We see this in the words *field* and *chief*.

> The vowels *ie* can be quite tricky and make the short-e sound. That is very tricky, isn't it? We see this in the word *friend*.

Look at the words below. Read each word out loud, then tell what sound the vowels *ie* make in the word.

pie   died

field   chief

friend

 **LET'S WRITE**

 **TEACHER NOTE**   • Save this page for the student to study for a future lesson.

Copy each word on the line next to it.

pie _____

died _____

field _____

chief _____

friend _____

LET'S REVIEW AND APPLY

Let's review the words you wrote in the last lesson.

pie   died
field   chief   friend

Do you remember how those vowels *ie* like to break the rules? They sure are tricky!

Let's review these tricky *ie* vowels! In our words for today, the *ie* vowels make three different sounds!

Remember:

- The vowels *ie* can follow the rule and make the long-i sound. We see this in the words *pie* and *died*.

TEACHER NOTE
- The student should read the word then spell it. Example: can c-a-n

- Read each word to the student. The student should spell the word, out loud, without looking. Go back and study the words until he or she can spell them from memory.

- The student may also write each word on an index card to practice. The student may create right-brain flashcards by drawing pictures on the cards or around the letters to help him or her remember how to spell the words.

- The vowels *ie* can trade with each other! Instead of the second vowel being silent and the first vowel saying its name, the FIRST vowel is silent, and the SECOND vowel says its name. That means the *i* stays silent and the *e* says its name! We see this in the words *field* and *chief*.

- The vowels *ie* can be quite tricky and make the short-e sound. That is very tricky, isn't it? We see this in the word *friend*.

Let's read each word again, but this time spell the word after you read it.

Now I am going to read each word to you. Let's see if you can remember how to spell it. It will be fun!

 PICTURE STUDY

Look at the pictures on pages 18–19 of *Not Too Small at All*.

(1) Describe the room on pages 18–19.

(2) Who are the mice in the bed?

(3) Who are the mice sitting on chairs?

(4) What is happening in the "cloud"?

(5) What is your favorite thing about the picture?

Spelling Fun!

Today we are going to spell words. There is a picture of each word we studied. Write the correct word under the picture.

1. _____

2. _____

3. _____

4. _____

5. _____

Some words end with the letters *ed*. In many words that end in *ed*, only the /d/ sound is heard. Listen to this word: *raced*. Raced ends in *ed*, but we only hear the /d/ sound.

Draw a line from the sentence to the matching picture.

Watch for words that end in the letters *ed*.

TEACHER NOTE
• Some students may need to read the sentences to the teacher before completing this section.

6. Dad waved a flag.

7. Sam drove the car.

8. Mom looked at the stars.

9. Jess chewed gum.

10. Dan wore a vest.

Word Fun!

Do you remember what a noun is? A noun is a person, place, or thing.

Can you tell me some nouns?

Now let's learn about a new kind of word. Let's learn about verbs.

TEACHER NOTE
- Let the student name some nouns. Practice different types of nouns if the student needs review.

Verbs show action.

Listen to this sentence and see if you can find the verb.

11. # The dog barked at the cat.

What word showed action?

Can you think of any verbs?

Good job!

TEACHER NOTE
- Allow the student to answer. Give clues if needed.
- Let the student name some verbs. Practice verbs if he or she has trouble identifying them.

12. Circle the pictures that show a verb.

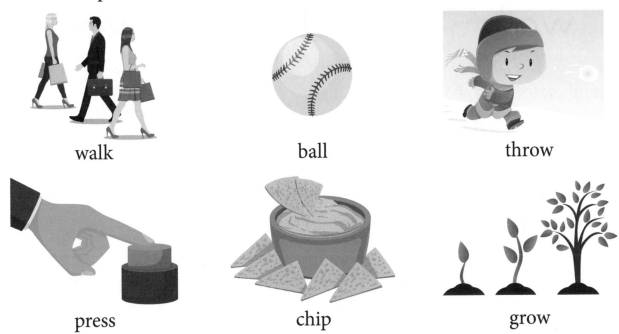

walk

ball

throw

press

chip

grow

 **CREATE YOUR OWN DICTIONARY!**

 **TEACHER NOTE** • Help the student read the words below.

Let's read the words you can put in your dictionary today.

family   lightning   rope

walk   water   wind

Remember, for each word you will:

- Find the page that has the same letter your word starts with.
- Write the word on the top line if empty or one of the other lines.
- Draw a picture that shows what the word means.
- Write a simple definition (or meaning) for the word.

READING TOGETHER

Do you remember what happened up to now in the story of *Not Too Small at All*? Narrate, or tell it, to me.

Let's read pages 20 and 21. You are going to read the first sentence.

TEACHER NOTE

- Review pages 4–19 if needed.

- Read pages 20–21 to the student. Be sure to point to each word as you read.

- Help the student sound out words if he or she has difficulty. Cover up part of a large word while the student sounds it out. Encourage him or her to sound out larger words. Have patience as the student sounds out the words. Tell him or her the word (showing how it is sounded out) and move on if there is sign of frustration.

- Student may read from the book or below.

She said her nāme was Ăbĭgāil and we ran down the hill togĕther ŭntĭl we rēached the ōpĕn door of the ark.

What happened in today's part of the story?
Can you tell it back to me?

Exercise 1 Day 41

REVIEW SIGHT WORDS

Review sight words using the flashcards created for words the student is still learning.

INDEPENDENT READING

 **PHONICS NEW & REVIEW**

Let's review words that use the letter combinations we have learned. Read each word as I point to it.

aghast	rough	dough
block	clock	flock
globe	plant	slide
brick	crate	dress
fruit	grape	prize
trick	write	

We are going to look at more words that are tricky. This time we will study words that have the vowels *ei* in the middle instead of *ie*.

There is a little poem we can learn that can help us remember when to use the vowel pair *ie* and when to use *ei*. Let's memorize it together.

i before *e* except after *c*, or when sounding like *a* as in *neighbor* and *weigh*.

The vowels *ei* are just like the vowel *ie*. They like to break the rules, too! Look at the first two words, *ceiling* and *seize*. The silent *i* makes the *e* say its name.

 **TEACHER NOTE**
• Point to the example words on the next page.

ceiling

seize

Now let's look at three words that break the rules. Remember our poem? *i* before *e* except after *c*, or when sounding like *a* as in *neighbor* and *weigh*? Did you notice the vowels *ei* can make the long-a sound? That is very tricky! We better keep a close eye on them! There are three words we are going to study where the vowels *ei* make the long-a sound: *eight*, *veil*, and *vein*.

eight

veil

vein

Look at the words below. Read each word out loud, then tell what sound the vowels *ei* make in the word. One of the words is tricky because it has silent letters. Remember, in some words the letters *gh* are silent. Watch out for them!

neighbor

weigh

 **LET'S WRITE**

 **TEACHER NOTE** • Save this page for the student to study for a future lesson.

Copy each word on the line next to it.

ceiling _____

seize _____

eight _____

veil _____

vein _____

 **LET'S REVIEW AND APPLY**   Let's review the words you wrote in the last lesson. We wrote words with the vowels *ei*.

ceiling   seize

eight   veil   vein

Do you remember our little poem that can help us remember when to use the vowels *ie* or *ei*?

i before *e* except after *c*, or when sounding like *a* as in *neighbor* and *weigh*.

Let's look at the first two words you wrote. The silent *i* makes the *e* say its name.

The *ei* in our last three words makes the long-a sound!

Those *ei* and *ie* vowels sure are tricky! We'd better keep a close eye on them!

Let's read each word again, but this time spell the word after you read it.

 **TEACHER NOTE**

- The student should read the word then spell it. Example: can c-a-n

- Read each word to the student. The student should spell the word, out loud, without looking. Go back and study the words until he or she can spell them from memory. If the student struggles, help him or her by giving the next letter.

- The student may also write each word on an index card to practice. The student may create right-brain flashcards by drawing pictures on the cards or around the letters to help him or her remember how to spell the words.

- The words in this section are trickier. Practice spelling them but move on if the student cannot master them.

Now I am going to read each word to you. Let's see if you can remember how to spell it. It will be fun!

PICTURE STUDY

Look at the pictures on pages 20–21 of *Not Too Small at All*.

(1) What is happening on page 20?

(2) What kinds of animals do you see?

(3) Describe the room on page 21.

(4) Who are the people?

(5) What is the mood of each of the mice?

(6) What is your favorite thing about the pictures?

Spelling Fun!

Today we are going to spell words. There is a picture of each word we studied. Write the correct word under the picture.

 **TEACHER NOTE** • The words in this lesson are found on page 126. The student may study them before completing this page.

_____

- - - - - - - - - - - - - - - - - - -

1. _____

2. _____

_____

- - - - - - - - - - - - - - - - - - -

3. _____

_____

- - - - - - - - - - - - - - - - - - -

4. _____

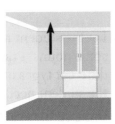

_____

- - - - - - - - - - - - - - - - - - -

5. _____

Draw a line from the sentence to the matching picture.
Remember to watch out for the silent letters *gh*.

6. Joe ate the cheese.

7. Sally gave me a treat.

8. Mommy will weigh the fruit.

9. Daddy made lunch.

10. The toast is hot.

Word Fun!

Do you remember what a noun is? A noun is a person, place, or thing.

Can you tell me some nouns?

TEACHER NOTE
- Let the student name some nouns. Practice different types of nouns if the student needs review.
- Let the student name some verbs. Practice verbs if he or she has trouble identifying them.

Do you remember what a verb is? Verbs show action. Can you think of any verbs?

Good job!

11.   Circle the pictures that show a verb.

cook   pig   raining

planting   seize   yawn

valley   can   look

CREATE YOUR OWN DICTIONARY!

TEACHER NOTE
• Help the student read the words below.

Let's read the words you can put in your dictionary today.

branch   cow   dove

float   raven   sing

Remember, for each word you will:

• Find the page that has the same letter your word starts with.

• Write the word on the top line if empty or one of the other lines.

• Draw a picture that shows what the word means.

• Write a simple definition (or meaning) for the word.

READING TOGETHER

Do you remember what happened up to now in the story of *Not Too Small at All*? Narrate, or tell it, to me.

Let's read page 22. You are going to read the first sentence.

TEACHER NOTE
- Review pages 4–21 if needed.

- Read page 22 to the student. Be sure to point to each word as you read.

- Help the student sound out words if he or she has difficulty. Cover up part of a large word while the student sounds it out. Encourage him or her to sound out larger words. Have patience as the student sounds out the words. Tell him or her the word (showing how it is sounded out) and move on if there is sign of frustration.

- Student may read from the book or below.

One day as I was wȧlkĭng through the ark, I hĕard a loud bawlĭng comĭng from one of the cȧttle stȧlls.

What happened in today's part of the story?
Can you tell it back to me?

Exercise 1 Day 46

REVIEW SIGHT WORDS

Review sight words using the flashcards created for words the student is still learning.

INDEPENDENT READING

PHONICS
NEW & REVIEW

Let's review words that use the letter combinations we have learned. Read each word as I point to it.

ghost	rough	high
block	clap	flock
glad	plant	sled
brick	crab	dress
frog	grape	press
trick	wrap	

We are going to look at more words that are tricky. Let's study words that use *oy* and *oi* to make the /oy/ sound.

TEACHER NOTE
• Point to the example words on the following page.

Many words use *oy* to make the /oy/ sound. Look at the first three words: *boy*, *joy*, and *toy*.

Some words use *oi* to make the /oy/ sound. Look at the last three words: *coin*, *soil*, and *oink*.

Look at the words below. Read each word out loud, then tell what letters are used to make the /oy/ sound in the word.

 **LET'S WRITE**

 **TEACHER NOTE** • Save this page for the student to study for a future lesson.

Copy each word on the line next to it.

boy   boy

joy   joy

toy   toy

coin   coin

soil   soil

oink   oink

 **LET'S REVIEW AND APPLY**

Let's review the words you wrote in the last lesson. We wrote words that use the letters *oy* and *oi* to make the /oy/ sound.

boy   joy   toy
coin   soil   oink

The first three words you wrote used the letters *oy* to make the /oy/ sound. The last three words you wrote used the letters *oi* to make the /oy/ sound.

Let's read each word again, but this time spell the word after you read it.

Now I am going to read each word to you. Let's see if you can remember how to spell it. It will be fun!

TEACHER NOTE

- The student should read the word then spell it. Example: can c-a-n

- Read each word to the student. The student should spell the word, out loud, without looking. Go back and study the words until he or she can spell them from memory. If the student struggles, help him or her by giving the next letter.

- The student may also write each word on an index card to practice. The student may create right-brain flashcards by drawing pictures on the cards or around the letters to help him or her remember how to spell the words.

PICTURE STUDY

Look at the pictures on pages 22–23 of *Not Too Small at All*.

(1) Describe the scene on pages 22–23.

(2) What kinds of animals are shown on page 22?

(3) What kind of food is shown?

(4) What is the mouse doing on page 23?

(5) What are the other animals doing on pages 22–23?

(6) What is your favorite thing about the pictures?

Spelling Fun!

Today we are going to spell words. There is a picture of each word we studied. Write the correct word under the picture.

TEACHER NOTE
- The words in this lesson are found on page 135. The student may study them before completing this page.

_____

- - - - - - - - - - - - - - - - - - -

1. _____

_____

- - - - - - - - - - - - - - - - - - -

2. _____

_____

- - - - - - - - - - - - - - - - - - -

3. _____

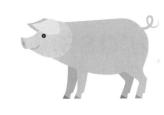
_____

- - - - - - - - - - - - - - - - - - -

4. _____

_____

- - - - - - - - - - - - - - - - - - -

5. _____

_____

- - - - - - - - - - - - - - - - - - -

6. _____

Some words end with the letters *ed*. In many words that end in *ed*, only the /d/ sound is heard. In some words, the letters *ed* sound like /ed/. Listen to this word: *handed*. Did you hear the /ed/ sound? Listen to the two sounds *ed* can make at the end of words: *handed, mailed*. Did you hear the two sounds? The word *handed* makes the /ed/ sound, but the word *mailed* makes the /d/ sound at the end.

> **TEACHER NOTE** • Some students may need to read the sentences to the teacher before completing this section.

Circle the correct word. Next, draw a line from the sentence to the matching picture. Watch for the words that end in the letters *ed*.

7. The (goat, gate) ate the grass.

8. The woman (planted, salted) a garden.

9. The child (ate, picked) the flower.

10. # The stone (is, did) heavy.

11. # The stars (shoe, shine) at night.

Word Fun!

Do you remember what a noun is? A noun is a person, place, or thing.

Can you tell me some nouns?

Do you remember what a verb is? Verbs show action. Can you think of any verbs?

Let's learn about a new kind of word.

TEACHER NOTE

- Let the student name some nouns. Practice different types of nouns if the student needs review.

- Let the student name some verbs. Practice verbs if he or she has trouble identifying them.

An adjective describes a noun. An adjective can be a color or can tell about size, texture, or shape. An adjective can also tell how many and how something smells, tastes, or sounds.

Listen to this sentence and see if you can find the adjective.

12. # The brown dog barked at the cat.

Can you think of any adjectives?

Good job!

TEACHER NOTE
- Allow the student to answer. Give clues if needed.
- Let the student name some adjectives. Practice adjectives if he or she has trouble identifying them. Be sure to talk about the different types of adjectives.

13. Circle the pictures that show an adjective.

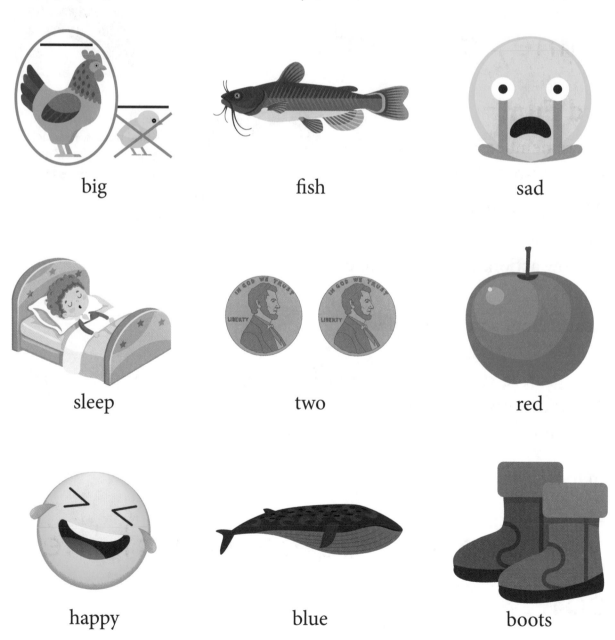

big

fish

sad

sleep

two

red

happy

blue

boots

 **CREATE YOUR OWN DICTIONARY!**

 **TEACHER NOTE** • Help the student read the words below.

Let's read the words you can put in your dictionary today.

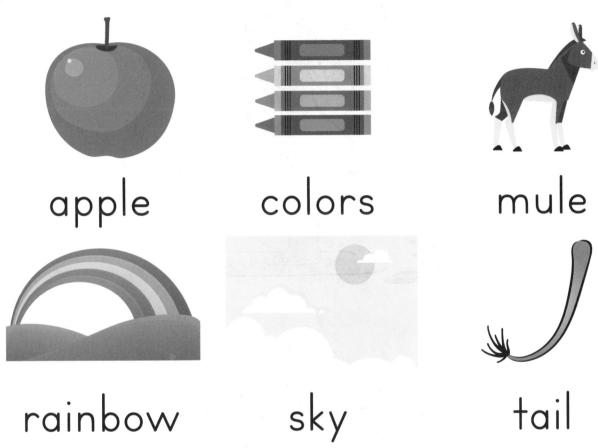

apple   colors   mule

rainbow   sky   tail

Remember, for each word you will:

- Find the page that has the same letter your word starts with.
- Write the word on the top line if empty or one of the other lines.
- Draw a picture that shows what the word means.
- Write a simple definition (or meaning) for the word.

Find and circle four differences between the pictures.

PICTURE STUDY

Let's take some time to study this picture.

(1) What is happening in this picture?

(2) Do you remember what Matthew 19 verses 13–15 tell us about Jesus blessing the children? Tell me what you remember. (Read the verses on page 63 if needed.)

(3) What colors are used in this picture?

(4) Describe how the people are dressed.

(5) How do you think Jesus feels?

(6) How do you think the children feel?

(7) How does the picture make you feel?

 **READING TOGETHER**

Do you remember what happened up to now in the story of *Not Too Small at All*? Narrate, or tell it, to me.

Let's read page 24. You are going to read the last sentence.

Now it is your turn to read!

 **TEACHER NOTE**   • Review pages 4–23 if needed.

• Read page 24 to the student. Be sure to point to each word as you read.

• Help the student sound out words if he or she has difficulty. Cover up part of a large word while the student sounds it out. Encourage him or her to sound out larger words. Have patience as the student sounds out the words. Tell him or her the word (showing how it is sounded out) and move on if there is sign of frustration.

• Student may read from the book or below.

The nĕxt tīme Nōah let the dove go we wāitĕd and wāitĕd, but she nĕver cāme băck and when it was tīme, God ōpĕned the ark's door.

What happened in today's part of the story? Can you tell it back to me?

 **REVIEW SIGHT WORDS**

Review sight words using the flashcards created for words the student is still learning.

 **INDEPENDENT READING**

PHONICS NEW & REVIEW

Let's review words that use the letter combinations we have learned. Read each word as I point to it.

pie	tried	died
field	chief	yield
friend	ceiling	seize
eight	veil	vein
boy	joy	toy
coin	soil	oink

We are going to look at more words that are tricky. Let's study words that use *ou* and *ow* to make the /ow/ sound.

TEACHER NOTE

• Point to the example words on the following page.

Many words use *ou* to make the /ow/ sound. Look at the first two words: *loud* and *mouse*.

Some words use *ow* to make the /ow/ sound. Look at the next two words: *plow* and *town*.

But wait! I see another rule breaker. Look at the last two words: *flow* and *grow*. The letters *ow* do not make the /ow/ sound. Instead, the *o* makes the long sound. It says its name.

What are we going to do with these rule breakers? We'd better keep a very close eye on them!

Look at the words below. Read each word out loud, then tell what letters are used to make /ow/ sound in the word and which words are rule breakers and make the long-o sound.

 LET'S WRITE

 TEACHER NOTE
• Save this page for the student to study for a future lesson.

Copy each word on the line next to it.

loud _____

mouse _____

plow _____

town _____

flow _____

grow _____

 **LET'S REVIEW AND APPLY**

Let's review the words you wrote in the last lesson. We wrote words that use the letters *ou* and *ow* to make the /ow/ sound. We also studied the rule breakers that use the letters *ow* to make the long-o sound.

loud   mouse

plow   town

flow   grow

The first two words you wrote used the letters *ou* to make the /ow/ sound. The next two words you wrote used the letters *ow* to make the /ow/ sound. The last two words you wrote are rule breakers. They used the letters *ow* to make the long-o sound.

Let's read each word again, but this time spell the word after you read it.

 **TEACHER NOTE**

- The student should read the word then spell it. Example: can c-a-n

- Read each word to the student. The student should spell the word, out loud, without looking. Go back and study the words until he or she can spell them from memory.

- The student may also write each word on an index card to practice. The student may create right-brain flashcards by drawing pictures on the cards or around the letters to help him or her remember how to spell the words.

Now I am going to read each word to you. Let's see if you can remember how to spell it. It will be fun!

PICTURE STUDY

Look at the pictures on pages 24–25 of *Not Too Small at All.*

(1) Describe the scene on pages 24–25.

(2) What kinds of animals are shown?

(3) Who is the man shown on page 25?

(4) What do you think the man is thinking?

(5) What is your favorite thing about the picture?

JUST 4 FUN!

Copy the drawing. Then write the name of the animal and the sound it makes.

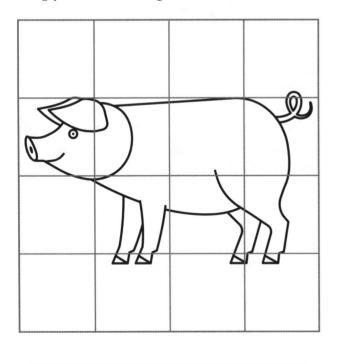

Spelling Fun!

Today we are going to spell words. There is a picture of each word we studied. Write the correct word under the picture.

TEACHER NOTE
- The words in this lesson are found on page 146. The student may study them before completing this page.

1. _____

2. _____

3. _____

4. _____

5. _____

6. _____

Circle the correct word then draw a line from the sentence to the matching picture.

TEACHER NOTE • Some students may need to read the sentences to the teacher before completing this section.

7. The mouse (rain, ran) from the cat.

8. The camel (drank, drink) from the bowl.

9. The tiger (lost, lived) in the jungle.

10. The ant (worked, walked) all summer.

11. The pig (reads, likes) to roll in mud.

150   Language Level 1 – Lesson 11

Word Fun!

Do you remember what a noun is? A noun is a person, place, or thing.

Can you tell me some nouns?

TEACHER NOTE
- Let the student name some nouns, verbs, and adjectives after each question. Practice different types of each if the student needs review.

Do you remember what a verb is? Verbs show action. Can you think of any verbs?

Do you remember what an adjective is? An adjective describes a noun. An adjective can be a color or can tell about size, texture, or shape. An adjective can also tell how many and how something smells, tastes, or sounds. Can you think of any adjectives?

Good job!

12. Circle the pictures that show an adjective.

fast   blue   blowing

laughing   three   small

 **CREATE YOUR OWN DICTIONARY!**

 **TEACHER NOTE** • Help the student read the words below.

Let's read the words you can put in your dictionary today.

Grand Canyon

hand

notebook

path

post

river

Remember, for each word you will:

- Find the page that has the same letter your word starts with.
- Write the word on the top line if empty or one of the other lines.
- Draw a picture that shows what the word means.
- Write a simple definition (or meaning) for the word.

 **READING TOGETHER**

Do you remember what happened up to now in the story of *Not Too Small at All*? Narrate, or tell it, to me.

Let's read page 26. You are going to read the first sentence.

 **TEACHER NOTE**

- Review pages 4–25 if needed.
- Read page 26 to the student. Be sure to point to each word as you read.
- Help the student sound out words if he or she has difficulty. Cover up part of a large word while the student sounds it out. Encourage him or her to sound out larger words. Have patience as the student sounds out the words. Tell him or her the word (showing how it is sounded out) and move on if there is sign of frustration.
- Student may read from the book or below.

It was a brănd new, frĕsh world rēborn by wåter.

What happened in today's part of the story?
Can you tell it back to me?

Exercise 1 Day 56

 **REVIEW SIGHT WORDS**

Review sight words using the flashcards created for words the student is still learning.

 **INDEPENDENT READING**

 **PHONICS NEW & REVIEW**

Let's review words that use the letter combinations we have learned. Read each word as I point to it.

pie	tried	died
field	chief	yield
friend	ceiling	seize
eight	veil	vein
boy	joy	toy
coin	soil	oink

We are going to look at more words that are tricky. Let's study words that have the vowels *oo* in them.

 **TEACHER NOTE**
• Point to the example words on the following page.

Let's look at the first three words on the next page. The first three words make the /oo/ sound as in *soon*: *food*, *moon*, and *boot*.

Let's look at the last three words on the next page. The vowels *oo* also make the /oo/ sound as in *good*: *cook*, *foot*, and *wood*.

Let's see if you can hear the two sounds *oo* makes in a word. Listen for the different middle sound each word makes: *soon*, *good*. Did you hear the different sounds *oo* makes?

Look at the words below. Read each word out loud, then tell what sound the letters *oo* make in the word.

LET'S WRITE

TEACHER NOTE
• Save this page for the student to study for a future lesson.

Copy each word on the line next to it.

food _____

moon _____

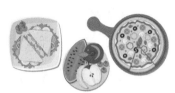

boot _____

cook _____

foot _____

wood _____

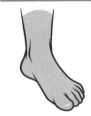

 **LET'S REVIEW AND APPLY**

Let's review the words you wrote in the last lesson. We wrote words that use the letters *oo* to make the /oo/ sound as in *soon* and the /oo/ sound as in *good*.

food   moon   boot

cook   foot   wood

Let's read each word again, but this time spell the word after you read it.

Now I am going to read each word to you. Let's see if you can remember how to spell it. It will be fun!

 **TEACHER NOTE**

- The student should read the word then spell it. Example: can c-a-n

- Read each word to the student. The student should spell the word, out loud, without looking. Go back and study the words until he or she can spell them from memory.

- The student may also write each word on an index card to practice. The student may create right-brain flashcards by drawing pictures on the cards or around the letters to help him or her remember how to spell the words.

 **PICTURE STUDY**

Look at the pictures on pages 26–27 of *Not Too Small at All.*

(1) Describe the scene on pages 26–27.

(2) What kinds of animals are shown?

(3) Who are the people shown on page 27?

(4) What is in the sky on pages 26–27?

(5) What is your favorite thing about the pictures?

Spelling Fun!

Today we are going to spell words. There is a picture of each word we studied. Write the correct word under the picture.

 **TEACHER NOTE**

• The words in this lesson are found on page 155. The student may study them before completing this page.

_____

- - - - - - - - - - - - - - -

1. _____

_____

- - - - - - - - - - - - - - -

2. _____

_____

- - - - - - - - - - - - - - -

3. _____

_____

- - - - - - - - - - - - - - -

4. _____

_____

- - - - - - - - - - - - - - -

5. _____

_____

- - - - - - - - - - - - - - -

6. _____

Circle the correct word then draw a line from the sentence to the matching picture.

TEACHER NOTE • Some students may need to read the sentences to the teacher before completing this section.

7. The cat (food, roof) dish was full.

8. The shining (spoon, moon) lit up the sky.

9. The owl began to (scoot, hoot) at night.

10. Wear a (hood, good) because it's cold.

11. The man started to (book, cook) our food.

Word Fun!

Do you remember what a noun is? A noun is a person, place, or thing.

Can you tell me some nouns?

TEACHER NOTE • Let the student name some nouns, verbs, and adjectives after each question. Practice different types of each if the student needs review.

Do you remember what a verb is? Verbs show action. Can you think of any verbs?

Do you remember what an adjective is? An adjective describes a noun. An adjective can be a color or can tell about size, texture, or shape. An adjective can also tell how many and how something smells, tastes, or sounds. Can you think of any adjectives?

Good job!

12. Circle the **nouns** with a **blue** crayon or pencil.

13. Circle the **verbs** with a **red** crayon or pencil.

14. Circle the adjectives with an orange crayon or pencil.

hot

cow

read

walk

car

long

song

ball

sat

bake

nine

red

 **CREATE YOUR OWN DICTIONARY!**

 **TEACHER NOTE**
- Help the student read the words below.

Let's read the words you can put in your dictionary today.

cliff   crab   creature

earth   eyes   love

Remember, for each word you will:

- Find the page that has the same letter your word starts with.
- Write the word on the top line if empty or one of the other lines.
- Draw a picture that shows what the word means.
- Write a simple definition (or meaning) for the word.

LET'S READ THE BIBLE

Luke 6 verses 27–31 tells us some things that Jesus taught. Listen carefully as I read the verses to you.

TEACHER NOTE
- You may use your own translation rather than NASB.

²⁷"But I say to you who hear, love your enemies, do good to those who hate you,

²⁸Bless those who curse you, pray for those who mistreat you.

²⁹Whoever hits you on the cheek, offer him the other also; and whoever takes away your coat, do not withhold your shirt from him either.

³⁰Give to everyone who asks of you, and whoever takes away what is yours, do not demand it back.

³¹Treat others the same way you want them to treat you.

ORAL NARRATION PRACTICE

TEACHER NOTE
- Allow the student to answer but take time to discuss the passage.

Let's think about what we read.

(1) Why do you think Jesus taught us to love our enemies and to do good to those who hate us?

(2) Why do you think Jesus said to bless those who say bad things about us and to pray for those who don't treat us nicely?

(3) What do you think it means to turn the other cheek?

(4) If someone takes something that belongs to you, would it be hard not to demand it back?

(5) The last verse is called the Golden Rule. Have you ever heard of it? Do you think it is a good way to live? Why or why not?

(6) Can you think of any ways God does these things for us?

 **READING TOGETHER**

Do you remember what happened up until now in the story of *Not Too Small at All*? Narrate, or tell it, to me.

Let's read the very last page of our story! Let's read page 28. Do you want to try to read the whole page if I help you with the hard words?

 **TEACHER NOTE**

- Review pages 4–27 if needed.

- Allow student to read the page if he or she wants; otherwise, let the student read the first sentence and any other sentence he or she wants to try to read. Keep it fun and encouraging even if the student isn't ready to read the whole page.

- Help the student sound out words if he or she has difficulty. Cover up part of a large word while the student sounds it out. Encourage him or her to sound out larger words. Have patience as the student sounds out the words. Tell him or her the word (showing how it is sounded out) and move on if there is sign of frustration.

What happened in today's part of the story? Can you tell it back to me?

 **REVIEW SIGHT WORDS**

Review sight words using the flashcards created for words the student is still learning.

 **INDEPENDENT READING**

You are doing great!

PHONICS
NEW & REVIEW

Let's review words that use the letter combinations we have learned. Read each word as I point to it.

found	loud	mouse
how	plow	town
flow	grow	
food	moon	boot
cook	foot	wood

PHONICS
NEW & REVIEW

Let's compare two words. The letters *ew* are tricky! They make two different sounds in these two words. They make the /oo/ sound as in the word *new*. They also make the /ū/ sound as in the word *view*.

TEACHER NOTE

- Allow student to read the new words and see if he or she can hear the two different sounds. Review them until he or she can hear the sounds.

Can you hear the two different sounds in these two words?

blew   few

Let's listen to the next two words. Can you find which word makes the /oo/ sound and which word makes the /yoo/ sound?

new   pew

Now let's look at the last word. The last word is another rule breaker! The *ew* makes the long-o sound in the word *sew*! We will have to remember that word.

sew

Look at the words below. Read each word out loud, then tell what sound the letters *ew* make in the word.

blew   new

few   pew

sew

LET'S WRITE

TEACHER NOTE

- Save this page for the student to study for a future lesson.

Copy each word on the line next to it.

blew _____

new _____

few _____

pew _____

sew _____

 **LET'S REVIEW AND APPLY**

Let's review the words you wrote in the last lesson. We wrote words that use the letters *ew* to make the /oo/ sound as in *too* and the /yoo/ sound as in *view*. We can't forget about the rule breaker that makes the long-o sound. Do you remember the word *sew*?

blew   new

few   pew   sew

Let's read each word again, but this time spell the word after you read it.

Now I am going to read each word to you. Let's see if you can remember how to spell it. It will be fun!

 **TEACHER NOTE**

- The student should read the word then spell it. Example: can c-a-n

- Read each word to the student. The student should spell the word, out loud, without looking. Go back and study the words until he or she can spell them from memory.

- The student may also write each word on an index card to practice. The student may create right-brain flashcards by drawing pictures on the cards or around the letters to help him or her remember how to spell the words.

 **PICTURE STUDY**

Look at the pictures on pages 28–29 of *Not Too Small at All.*

(1) Describe the scene on pages 28–29.

(2) Where do you think the mice made their home that is shown in the picture?

(3) Who are the mice shown?

(4) Who are the people shown on page 29?

(5) What are the people doing?

(6) What is your favorite thing about the pictures?

Spelling Fun!

Today we are going to spell words. There is a picture of each word we studied. Write the correct word under the picture.

🍎 **TEACHER NOTE**

• The words in this lesson are found on page 165. The student may study them before completing this page.

1. _____

2. _____

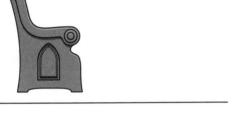

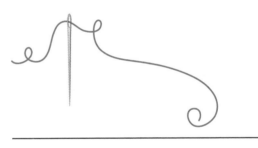

3. _____

4. _____

5. _____

Circle the correct word then draw
a line from the sentence to the
matching picture.

6. I will (stank, stack) the blocks.

7. You (blink, blank) your eyes.

8. They (look, like) milk to drink.

9. He (swims, saves) in the pool.

10. She has (saved, jumped) her coins.

Word Fun!

Do you remember what a noun is? A noun is a person, place, or thing.

Can you tell me some nouns?

TEACHER NOTE
- Let the student name some nouns, verbs, and adjectives after each question. Practice different types of each if the student needs review.

Do you remember what a verb is? Verbs show action. Can you think of any verbs?

Do you remember what an adjective is? An adjective describes a noun. An adjective can be a color or can tell about size, texture, or shape. An adjective can also tell how many and how something smells, tastes, or sounds. Can you think of any adjectives?

Good job!

11. Circle the **nouns** with a **blue** crayon or pencil.

12. Circle the **verbs** with a **red** crayon or pencil.

13. Circle the **adjectives** with an **orange** crayon or pencil.

cold   stack   milk

coins   green   salty

save   swim   look

blocks   gold   pool

 **CREATE YOUR OWN DICTIONARY!**

 **TEACHER NOTE** • Help the student read the words below.

Let's read the words you can put in your dictionary today.

animal   in   light

open   queen   tent

Remember, for each word you will:

• Find the page that has the same letter your word starts with.

• Write the word on the top line if empty or one of the other lines.

• Draw a picture that shows what the word means.

• Write a simple definition (or meaning) for the word.

READING TOGETHER

Optional: Read *Charlie and Trike in the Grand Canyon Adventure* to the student.

Read pages 1–5 of *Charlie and Trike in the Grand Canyon Adventure*. Take turns reading the pages with the student. Be sure to read the flip-out pages.

What happened in today's part of the story? Can you tell it back to me?

REVIEW SIGHT WORDS

Let's read through our sight words.

TEACHER NOTE
- You may take turns reading sentences, or you may pick out shorter words and have the student read them. If the student is reading well and has the stamina, he or she may do all of the reading.
- Help the student sound out words if he or she has difficulty. The student may come across new sounds or silent letters as he or she reads. Show how the word is sounded out and then let the student read the word. Encourage him or her to sound out larger words. Cover up part of a large word while the student sounds it out. Have patience as the student sounds out the words. Tell him or her the word (showing how it is sounded out) and move on if there is sign of frustration.

TEACHER NOTE
- The student should easily read the sight words by now.
- Allow student to read the sight words to you.

and an as at

in is it if

did of on not

Continued on the next page.

a	I	be	see
all	but	to	for
from	or	so	no
are	he	was	his
how	can	we	had
will	has	get	the
that	this	than	when
what	who	then	them
they	out	she	have
you	by	my	belong

I am going to read a word, and then you are going to spell it.

and	an	as	at
in	is	it	if
did	of	on	

Today's lesson is over, but we may read together the special feature on page 4 of *Charlie and Trike* if you want to.

 **INDEPENDENT READING**

PHONICS NEW & REVIEW

Let's review words that use the letter combinations we have learned. Read each word as I point to it.

found   loud   mouse

how   plow   town

flow   grow

food   moon   boot

cook   foot   wood

Let's review the sounds some letter combinations make. First, I am going to say the letters; then I am going to make the sound the letters make together. Next, I will read a word that has the sound; then you will read a word that has the sound.

TEACHER NOTE

- Some of the letters/sounds were covered in *Foundations Phonics*. If the student hasn't learned the sounds, please take time to practice with him or her. New letters/sounds covered in this lesson are indicated with an asterisk (*).

Before we begin, do you remember what sound we learned the letters *ou* can make? Right! The letters *ou* can make the /ow/ sound! Now we are going to learn about more sounds the letters *ou* can make.

Letters	Sounds Like	As In	Read
ou	/oo/	could	would
ou	/ü/	through	croup
*ou	/ō/	four	your
*ou	/ŭ/	enough	touch

Write the missing letters for each word.

1. w_____ld

2. cr_____p

3. y_____r

4. t_____ch

LET'S WRITE

Let's write a sentence about Charlie and Trike.

Remember to use your best handwriting! Be sure to leave space between your words so that you can read back your sentences easily. It helps to put a finger after each word to see how much space you should leave.

Charlie and Trike made their way to the Grand Canyon.

Copy the sentence on the lines.

charlie and Trike made their way to the grand canyon

 **LET'S REVIEW AND APPLY**   Let's read the sentence you wrote in the last lesson.

Chårlie and Trīke māde their way to the Grănd Cănyŏn.

All sentences have some things in common. The first word in a sentence begins with a capital letter.

Sentences also end in punctuation. Punctuation can be a period, exclamation point, or question mark.

 **TEACHER NOTE**
- Point to examples in the sentence the student wrote.
- Allow the student to find sentences that end in a period, exclamation point, and question mark.

Let's find some punctuation marks on page 1 of *Charlie and Trike in the Grand Canyon Adventure*. Let's see if we can find a sentence that ends with a period. A period is a dot. Most sentences end with a period. Can you find one?

Sentences that say something exciting end in an exclamation point. An exclamation point looks like this: ! Can you find a sentence on page 1 that ends with an exclamation point?

Sentences that ask a question end in a question mark. A question mark looks like this: ? To find a sentence with a question mark, we need to jump ahead in our story to page 6. Can you find a sentence on page 6 that ends with a question mark?

Let's pick some words from *Charlie and Trike in the Grand Canyon Adventure* to use as our spelling words and write them on the next page.

 **TEACHER NOTE**
- Help the student pick 5 short words from pages 1–3 to use as spelling words. If you have trouble picking the words, you may use the number words: **one**, **two**, **three**, **four**, **five**. For your reference, be sure to write the words you have chosen in the back of the book in the list of spelling words.

_____   _____

-          -

1. _____   2. _____

_____   _____

-          -

3. _____   4. _____

_____

- - - - - - - - - - - - - - - - - - - -

5. _____

Study the spelling words you picked out.

Now I am going to read each word to you. Let's see if you can remember how to spell it. It will be fun!

 **TEACHER NOTE**
- Allow the student time to study the words.

- Read each word to the student. The student should spell the word, out loud, without looking. Go back and study the words until he or she can spell them from memory.

- The student may also write each word on an index card to practice. The student may create right-brain flashcards by drawing pictures on the cards or around the letters to help him or her remember how to spell the words.

 **PICTURE STUDY**

Look at the pictures on pages 1–5 of *Charlie and Trike in the Grand Canyon Adventure.*

(1) Describe to me the picture on the first page. Include the details you see.

(2) What is happening in the pictures on pages 2–4?

(3) What animals do you see?

(4) What colors are used?

(5) There is a lot happening on page 5. Describe what you see.

(6) What is your favorite picture from the pages we have looked at today?

Sentence Fun!

Today we are going to work with sentences. Choose the correct word and write it at the beginning of the sentence.

Barns   Cars   Dad

Dogs   Fish

_____

1. _____ went to work.

2. _____ drive fast.

3. _____ like to bark.

4. _____ can swim.

5. _____ are for animals.

 **CREATE YOUR OWN DICTIONARY!**

 **TEACHER NOTE** • Help the student read the words below.

Let's read the words you can put in your dictionary today.

ant   day   edge

green   jump   x-ray

Remember, for each word you will:

- Find the page that has the same letter your word starts with.
- Write the word on the top line if empty or one of the other lines.
- Draw a picture that shows what the word means.
- Write a simple definition (or meaning) for the word.

PICTURE
STUDY

We do not know the artist of this horse picture. This picture also doesn't have a title. Let's give this picture a title. You can name it anything you want. Write it below.

TEACHER NOTE

• Student may need help spelling his or her title.

_____

- -

_____

This picture uses a shape pattern to create the picture.

(1) What shapes do you see?

(2) What colors are used?

(3) Find and point to the reflection of the horse.

(4) Is the horse running or standing still? How do you know?

(5) What do you like about this picture?

READING TOGETHER

Do you remember what happened in the first part of the story of *Charlie and Trike in the Grand Canyon Adventure*? Narrate, or tell it, to me.

Let's read pages 6–9 of *Charlie and Trike in the Grand Canyon Adventure*. Take turns reading the pages with me.

What happened in today's part of the story? Can you tell it back to me?

REVIEW SIGHT WORDS

Let's study how to spell some of our sight words.

I am going to read a word, and then you are going to spell it.

TEACHER NOTE
- Review pages 1–5 if needed.

- You may take turns reading sentences, or you may pick out shorter words and have the student read them. If the student is reading well and has the stamina, he or she may do all of the reading.

- Be sure to lift the flap and read the text on page 9.

- Help the student sound out words if he or she has difficulty. The student may come across new sounds or silent letters as he or she reads. Show how the word is sounded out and then let the student read the word. Encourage him or her to sound out larger words. Cover up part of a large word while the student sounds it out. Have patience as the student sounds out the words. Tell him or her the word (showing how it is sounded out) and move on if there is sign of frustration.

TEACHER NOTE
- The student should easily read the sight words by now. He or she may study the words below before trying to spell them.

- Read the eleven sight words on the next page, one at a time, allowing the student to spell the word.

- You may create flashcards out of any words the student finds difficult to spell and have him or her practice them regularly.

not   a   I

be   see   all

but   to   for

from   or

Today's lesson is over, but we may read together the special feature on page 6 of *Charlie and Trike* if you want to.

TEACHER NOTE • Read the locations on the Grand Canyon Map to the student and have him or her point to the locations on the map if interested.

INDEPENDENT READING

PHONICS NEW & REVIEW

Let's review words that use the letter combinations we have learned. Read each word as I point to it.

blew	new
few	pew
sew	
could	would
through	croup
four	your
enough	touch

Let's study some new letter combinations. Let's look at what happens when we add a consonant after the letter *s*.

TEACHER NOTE
- Two of the letter combinations have been studied in previous lessons. They are marked with an asterisk (*).

Letters	Sounds Like	As In	Read
sc	/sc/	scout	scår
sk	/sk/	skate	skŭnk
*sl	/sl/	sling	slīme
sm	/sm/	smell	smōke
sn	/sn/	snow	snăp
*sp	/sp/	spot	spěnd
st	/st/	stop	stĭng
sw	/sw/	swing	swĭm

Name_____

Write the missing letters for each word.

1. _____**ar**

2. _____**unk**

3. _____**ime**

4. _____**oke**

5. _____**ap**

6. _____**end**

7. _____**ing**

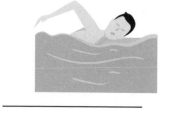

8. _____**im**

LET'S WRITE

Let's write a sentence about Charlie and Trike. Start your sentence with a capital letter. Start each name with a capital letter. Add a period at the end.

Remember to use your best handwriting! Be sure to leave space between your words so that you can read back your sentences easily. It helps to put a finger after each word to see how much space you should leave.

Trike pulled Charlie back onto the trail.

Copy the sentence on the lines.

LET'S REVIEW AND APPLY

Let's read the sentence you wrote in the last lesson.

Trīke pulled Chårliē băck onto the trāil.

Remember:

- The first word in a sentence begins with a capital letter.
- Sentences end with a period, exclamation point, or question mark.

Did you remember to start your sentence with a capital letter? What punctuation mark did your sentence end with?

Let's look at the sentences on pages 6–9 of *Charlie and Trike in the Grand Canyon Adventure.*

Find and point to a sentence that ends with a period.

Find one that ends with an exclamation point.

Find a sentence that ends with a question mark.

Did you remember that the first letter of a name is a capital letter?

Let's find the names on pages 6–9 of *Charlie and Trike in the Grand Canyon Adventure*! As we find the names, tell me what letter is a capital letter.

Did you remember that the first letter of a place is a capital letter? Some places have a name that includes more than one word.

Let's find the name of a place on page 6 of *Charlie and Trike in the Grand Canyon Adventure*! The place we are looking for has two words. Each word begins with a capital letter. Can you tell me the name of the place and the capital letter in each word?

Let's pick some words from *Charlie and Trike in the Grand Canyon Adventure* to use as our spelling words and write them below.

1. _____   2. _____

3. _____   4. _____

5. _____

Study the spelling words you picked out.

Now I am going to read each word to you. Let's see if you can remember how to spell it. It will be fun!

 **TEACHER NOTE**
- Allow the student time to study the words.

- Read each word to the student. The student should spell the word, out loud, without looking. Go back and study the words until he or she can spell them from memory.

- The student may also write each word on an index card to practice. The student may create right-brain flashcards by drawing pictures on the cards or around the letters to help him or her remember how to spell the words.

 **PICTURE STUDY**

Look at the pictures on pages 6–9 of *Charlie and Trike in the Grand Canyon Adventure.*

(1) What is happening in the pictures on page 6?

(2) How many people do you see?

(3) How many animals do you see?

(4) Describe what you see happening on page 7.

(5) What is happening on page 8?

(6) Describe the expressions (or emotions) on the animals' faces.

(7) What is happening in the picture on page 9?

(8) What is happening when you open the flap?

(9) What is your favorite picture from the pages we have looked at today?

Sentence Fun!

Today we are going to work with sentences.

Choose the correct word and write it at the beginning of the sentence. Add the correct punctuation at the end of each sentence.

Birds   Come   Get

Mom   Where   Who

1. _____ pets the cat

2. _____ are you going

3. _____ here quickly

4. _____ can fly

5. _____ out of the way

6. _____ is going with us

Circle the correct word or words in each sentence.

7. We took a trip to (New York, ohio).

8. (david, Jess) went to church.

9. (I, i) like to read books.

10. We can go to the (Zoo, zoo).

11. We will go to the city of (Erie, erie).

 JUST **4** FUN!

Match each shape to its shadow. Then write the name of the animal and the sound it makes.

_____   _____

- - - - - - - - - - - - - - - - - -   - - - - - - - - - - - - - - - - - -

_____   _____

 **CREATE YOUR OWN DICTIONARY!**

 **TEACHER NOTE** • Help the student read the words below.

Let's read the words you can put in your dictionary today.

iguana   jeans   jelly

king   quack   trout

Remember, for each word you will:

• Find the page that has the same letter your word starts with.

• Write the word on the top line if empty or one of the other lines.

• Draw a picture that shows what the word means.

• Write a simple definition (or meaning) for the word.

READING TOGETHER

Do you remember what happened up to now in the story of *Charlie and Trike in the Grand Canyon Adventure*? Narrate, or tell it, to me.

Let's read pages 10–13 of *Charlie and Trike in the Grand Canyon Adventure*. Take turns reading the pages with me.

TEACHER NOTE

• Review pages 1–9 if needed.

• Help the student sound out words if he or she has difficulty. The student may come across new sounds or silent letters as he or she reads. Show how the word is sounded out and then let the student read the word. Encourage him or her to sound out larger words. Cover up part of a large word while the student sounds it out. Have patience as the student sounds out the words. Tell him or her the word (showing how it is sounded out) and move on if there is sign of frustration.

What happened in today's part of the story? Can you tell it back to me?

REVIEW SIGHT WORDS

I am going to read a word, and then you are going to spell it.

TEACHER NOTE

- The student should easily read the sight words by now. He or she may study the words below before trying to spell them.

- You may create flashcards out of any words the student finds difficult to spell and have him or her practice them regularly.

so	no	are	he
was	his	how	can
we	had		

Today's lesson is over, but we may read together the special features on pages 10, 11, and 12 of *Charlie and Trike* if you want to.

TEACHER NOTE

- Read My Green Notebook on page 10, the two flap sections on page 11, and Let's Talk About Noah's Flood on page 12 if interested.

INDEPENDENT READING

PHONICS NEW & REVIEW

Let's review words that use the letter combinations we have learned. Read each word as I point to it.

blew   new

few   pew

sew

could   would

through   croup

four   your

enough   touch

Let's study some new letter combinations. Let's look at vowel combinations that start with the letter *a*.

TEACHER NOTE

- Many letter combinations have been studied in *Foundations Phonics*. In this section, the student will be studying new combinations, marked with an asterisk (*).

Letters	Sounds Like	As In	Read
*al	/aw/	talk	walk
*au	/aw/	haul	autō
*aw	/aw/	draw	claw
*ay	/ā/	play	pray

Write the missing letters for each word.

1. w_____k

2. _____to

3. cl_____

4. pr_____

Do you remember this rule about the silent-e? The silent-e at the end of the word makes the vowel say its name.

The second vowel in a word can make the first vowel say its name. When that happens, the second vowel is silent, just as it is with the silent-e at the end of a word. Let's study some examples.

TEACHER NOTE

- The letter combination *ai* has been studied in *Foundations Phonics*. The new combinations are marked with an asterisk (*).

- The letter combination *ea* has been studied in Lesson 4. The new combinations are marked with an asterisk (*).

Letters	Sounds Like	As In	Read
*ai	/ā/	pain	mail
ea	/ē/	bean	peach
*oa	/ō/	boat	toad
*oe	/ō/	toe	foe
*ee	/ē/	deer	seed

Write the missing letters for each word.

5. m_____l

6.  p_____ch

7. t_____d

8. f_____

9. s_____d

LET'S WRITE

Let's write a sentence about Charlie and Trike.

Remember to use your best handwriting! Be sure to leave space between your words so that you can read back your sentences easily. It helps to put a finger after each word to see how much space you should leave.

Trike told Charlie about a flood.

Copy the sentence on the lines.

_____

- -

_____

_____

- -

_____

_____

- -

_____

 LET'S REVIEW AND APPLY

Let's read the sentence you wrote in the last lesson.

Trīke tōld Chȧrliē about a flood.

Remember:

- The first word in a sentence begins with a capital letter.
- Sentences end with a period, exclamation point, or question mark.
- The names of nouns begin with a capital letter.

Did you remember to start your sentence with a capital letter? What punctuation mark did your sentence end with?

Let's talk about punctuation! As we learned, a sentence can end in a period, question mark, or exclamation point.

Most sentences end with a period. A sentence that makes a statement or tells something ends with a period. Let's look at page 10 of *Charlie and Trike in the Grand Canyon Adventure.* Find a sentence that ends with a period and show it to me.

 **TEACHER NOTE** • Read each sentence to the student as he or she finds them.

A question mark is at the end of a sentence that asks a question. Look back on page 9 and find the sentence that ends with a question mark.

An exclamation point is at the end of a sentence to show excitement.

Let's go back to page 7 and find a sentence that ends with an exclamation point.

Let's pick some words from *Charlie and Trike in the Grand Canyon Adventure* to use as our spelling words and write them below.

TEACHER NOTE
- Help the student pick 5 short words from pages 10–13 to use as spelling words. If you have trouble picking the words, you may use these words: **time, whole, true, God, Earth**. For your reference, be sure to write the words you have chosen in the back of the book in the list of spelling words.

1. _____

2. _____

3. _____

4. _____

5. _____

Study the spelling words you picked out.

Now I am going to read each word to you. Let's see if you can remember how to spell it. It will be fun!

TEACHER NOTE
- Allow the student time to study the words.

- Read each word to the student. The student should spell the word, out loud, without looking. Go back and study the words until he or she can spell them from memory.

- The student may also write each word on an index card to practice. The student may create right-brain flashcards by drawing pictures on the cards or around the letters to help him or her remember how to spell the words.

PICTURE STUDY

Look at the pictures on pages 10–13 of *Charlie and Trike in the Grand Canyon Adventure*.

(1) Describe what is happening on page 10.

(2) How would you describe the expression (or emotion) on Charlie's face? How about Trike's face?

(3) Describe what you see happening on page 11.

(4) How would you describe the expression (or emotion) on Charlie's face? How about Trike's face?

(5) What is happening on page 12?

(6) What is Charlie doing on page 13?

(7) What is your favorite picture from the pages we have looked at today?

Reading is fun!

Sentence Fun!

Today we are going to work with sentences.

A sentence must end in a punctuation mark:

| a period **.** | question mark **?** | exclamation point **!** |

Add the correct punctuation to each sentence.

1. Where did you go

2. My mom gave me a hug

3. Who lost their coat

4. I did it

5. That is hot

6. My dog likes to run

Circle the correct word in each sentence.

7. Where did (Charlie, charlie) go?

8. (God, god) loves me.

9. We learn about (jesus, Jesus) at church.

10. The (Boy, boy) sat next to me.

11. My church is on (main, Main) Street.

 JUST **4** FUN!

Draw the item that comes next in each pattern.

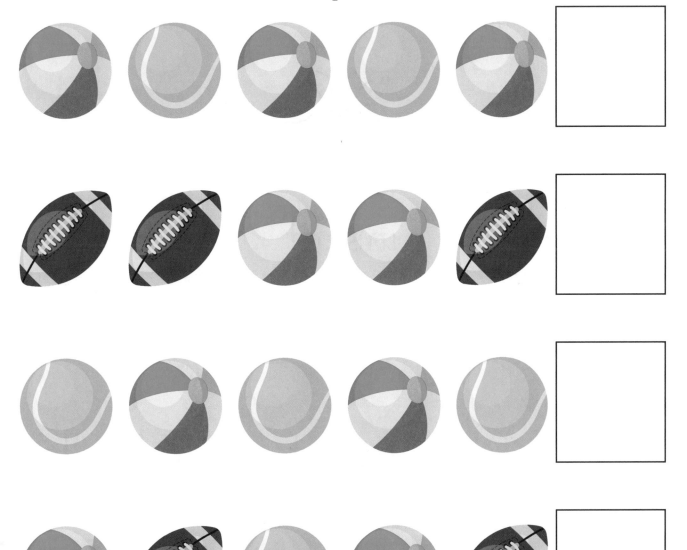

 **CREATE YOUR OWN DICTIONARY!**

 **TEACHER NOTE** • Help the student read the words below.

Let's read the words you can put in your dictionary today.

give   insect   key

kid   quart   umbrella

Remember, for each word you will:

• Find the page that has the same letter your word starts with.

• Write the word on the top line if empty or one of the other lines.

• Draw a picture that shows what the word means.

• Write a simple definition (or meaning) for the word.

 **LET'S READ A POEM**

I am going to read a poem to you.
Listen carefully as I read it.

"Now We Are Six"
By A.A. Milne

When I was One,
I had just begun.

When I was Two,
I was nearly new.

When I was Three
I was hardly me.

When I was Four,
I was not much more.

When I was Five,
I was just alive.

But now I am Six,
I'm as clever as clever,
So, I think I'll be six now for ever and ever.

This poem is called "Now We Are Six." It was printed in a book in the year 1927. That was a long time ago, but we can still enjoy it today.

A.A. Milne is the author of the poem. That means he wrote it. He also wrote a famous book called *Winnie the Pooh*.

Let's study this poem. This poem has words that rhyme. Two words that rhyme sound the same at the end of the word. In the first part of the poem, the words *one* and *begun* rhyme. Do you hear how they sound the same?

Now We Are Six is a book of 35 children's verses by A.A. Milne, with illustrations by E.H. Shepard. It was first published in 1927.

I am going to read each section to you. After I read each section, tell me which words rhyme! When I get to the last section, listen carefully because there are three lines instead of two and only two of the lines rhyme.

TEACHER NOTE
- Read the first two lines to the student and emphasize the words *one* and *begun*.
- Read each section to the student, emphasizing the rhyming words. Pause after each section to allow the student to identify the words that rhyme.

I'm going to read the poem to you one more time.

ORAL NARRATION PRACTICE

TEACHER NOTE
- Allow the student to answer but take time to discuss the poem.

Let's think about what we read.

(1) What is the poem about?

(2) What does the author think about being six?

(3) What do you think of this poem? Do you like it?

(4) What do you think of how it ends? Would you end it differently? If so, how would you end it?

READING TOGETHER

TEACHER NOTE
- Review pages 1–13 if needed.

- Help the student sound out words if he or she has difficulty. The student may come across new sounds or silent letters as he or she reads. Show how the word is sounded out and then let the student read the word. Encourage him or her to sound out larger words. Cover up part of a large word while the student sounds it out. Have patience as the student sounds out the words. Tell him or her the word (showing how it is sounded out) and move on if there is sign of frustration.

Do you remember what happened up to now in the story of *Charlie and Trike in the Grand Canyon Adventure*? Narrate, or tell it, to me.

Let's read pages 14–17 of *Charlie and Trike in the Grand Canyon Adventure*. Take turns reading the pages with me.

What happened in today's part of the story? Can you tell it back to me?

REVIEW SIGHT WORDS

I am going to read a word, and then you are going to spell it.

TEACHER NOTE

- The student should easily read the sight words by now. He or she may study the words below before trying to spell them.
- You may create flashcards out of any words the student finds difficult to spell and have him or her practice them regularly.

will has get the

that this than when

what who

Today's lesson is over, but we may read together the special feature on page 14 of *Charlie and Trike* if you want to.

TEACHER NOTE

- Read Grand Canyon Rock Layers on page 14 if interested.

INDEPENDENT READING

PHONICS NEW & REVIEW

Let's review words that use the letter combinations we have learned. Read each word as I point to it.

scout	scar	skate
skunk	sling	slime
smell	smoke	snow
snap	spot	spend
stop	sting	swing
talk	walk	haul
auto	draw	claw
play	pray	

Let's study some new letter combinations. Let's look at combinations that have 3 letters!

Letters	Sounds Like	As In	Read
str	/str/	strip	straw
spr	/spr/	sprout	spray
scr	/scr/	scrub	screw
spl	/spl/	splash	split

Write the missing letters for each word.

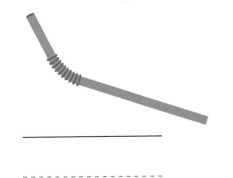

1. _____aw

2. _____ay

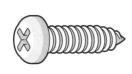

3. _____ew

4. _____it

 **LET'S WRITE**

Let's write sentences about Charlie and Trike.

Remember to use your best handwriting! Be sure to leave space between your words so that you can read back your sentences easily. It helps to put a finger after each word to see how much space you should leave.

Charlie fell into the river! He was scared.

Copy the sentences on the lines.

 **LET'S REVIEW AND APPLY**

Let's read the sentences you wrote in the last lesson.

Chårliē fĕll ĭnto the rĭver! He was scāred.

Remember:

- The first word in a sentence begins with a capital letter.
- Sentences end with a period, exclamation point, or question mark.

Did you remember to start each sentence with a capital letter? What punctuation marks did your sentences end with?

Do you remember what kind of a sentence has a period at the end? A sentence that makes a statement or tells something ends with a period. We call this type of sentence a declarative sentence. It declares something. Declare is a word that means to make a statement or to tell something. What do we call a sentence that makes a statement? Yes, it is called a declarative sentence.

Tell me a declarative sentence.

 **TEACHER NOTE** • The student may need some help coming up with a sentence that ends with a period, a question mark, and an exclamation point. Assist as needed.

Do you remember what kind of a sentence ends in a question mark? A sentence that asks a question ends with a question mark. We call a sentence that asks a question an interrogative sentence. That's a big word! It has the word *interrogate* in it. Interrogate means to question. What do we call a sentence that asks a question? Yes, it is called an interrogative sentence.

Tell me an interrogative sentence.

Do you remember what kind of a sentence ends in an exclamation point? A sentence that shows excitement ends in an exclamation point. We call a sentence that ends with an exclamation point an exclamatory sentence. Exclamatory is a big word, too! It has the word *exclaim* in it. Exclaim means to say something in an excited way. What do we call a sentence that shows excitement? Yes, it is called an exclamatory sentence.

Tell me an exclamatory sentence.

Let's pick some words from *Charlie and Trike in the Grand Canyon Adventure* to use as our spelling words and write them below.

 **TEACHER NOTE**
- Help the student pick 5 short words from pages 14–17 to use as spelling words. If you have trouble picking the words, you may use these words: **coals, next, trout, help, feet**. For your reference, be sure to write the words you have chosen in the back of the book in the list of spelling words.

1. _____

2. _____

3. _____

4. _____

5. _____

Study the spelling words you picked out.

Now I am going to read each word to you. Let's see if you can remember how to spell it. It will be fun!

TEACHER NOTE

- Allow the student time to study the words.

- Read each word to the student. The student should spell the word, out loud, without looking. Go back and study the words until he or she can spell them from memory.

- The student may also write each word on an index card to practice. The student may create right-brain flashcards by drawing pictures on the cards or around the letters to help him or her remember how to spell the words.

 **PICTURE STUDY**

Look at the pictures on pages 14–17 of *Charlie and Trike in the Grand Canyon Adventure.*

(1) Describe what is happening on page 14.

(2) What is happening in the background of page 15?

(3) What is happening in the middle of the picture?

(4) What is happening in the foreground (front) of the picture?

(5) Why was Charlie scowling?

(6) Describe page 16.

(7) What is happening on page 17?

(8) What is your favorite picture from the pages we have looked at today?

Sentence Fun!

A sentence has two parts. It has a subject and a predicate.

Often the first part of a sentence tells what or whom the sentence is about. This is called the subject. Every sentence has a subject.

A sentence also needs to tell what the subject does or is. This is called a predicate.

I am going to read a sentence to you. Listen carefully.

The dog ran outside.

What is the subject of the sentence? Yes, the subject is *the dog*. The dog is what the sentence is about.

Can you tell me what the predicate is? Remember, the predicate tells what the subject does or is. Yes, the predicate is *ran outside*. We know what the dog did. It ran outside.

Study each sentence and make sure it has both a subject and predicate. Circle the complete sentences.

1. # Charlie kicked a rock.

2. # Ate the apple.

3. # Swings the rope.

4. # I went outside to play.

5. # We ate soup for lunch.

Circle the correct word in each sentence. Draw a line to the correct picture.

6. We (had, has) a fun time at the park.

7. We (are, have) going to church.

8. He (baking, baked) a cake.

9. He (swims, saves) in the pool.

10. I (were, was) going to take the dog for a walk.

 **CREATE YOUR OWN DICTIONARY!**

 **TEACHER NOTE** • Help the student read the words below.

Let's read the words you can put in your dictionary today.

ice   jungle   kick

net   up   visit

Remember, for each word you will:

- Find the page that has the same letter your word starts with.
- Write the word on the top line if empty or one of the other lines.
- Draw a picture that shows what the word means.
- Write a simple definition (or meaning) for the word.

READING TOGETHER

Do you remember what happened up to now in the story of *Charlie and Trike in the Grand Canyon Adventure*? Narrate, or tell it, to me.

Let's read pages 18–23 of *Charlie and Trike in the Grand Canyon Adventure*. Take turns reading the pages with me.

What happened in today's part of the story? Can you tell it back to me?

TEACHER NOTE
- Review pages 1–17 if needed.
- Help the student sound out words if he or she has difficulty. The student may come across new sounds or silent letters as he or she reads. Show how the word is sounded out and then let the student read the word. Encourage him or her to sound out larger words. Cover up part of a large word while the student sounds it out. Have patience as the student sounds out the words. Tell him or her the word (showing how it is sounded out) and move on if there is sign of frustration.

Exercise 1   Day 86

REVIEW SIGHT WORDS

I am going to read a word, and then you are going to spell it.

TEACHER NOTE
- The student should easily read the sight words by now. He or she may study the words below before trying to spell them.

then   them   they   out

she   have   you   by

my   belong

INDEPENDENT READING

PHONICS NEW & REVIEW

Let's study some new letter combinations. Let's look at combinations that have 3 letters again. They make a new sound when they are together!

Letters	Sounds Like	As In	Read
squ	/squ/	squad	squid
thr	/thr/	three	throw
dge	/j/	edge	judge
tch	/ch/	itch	hatch

Write the missing letters for each word.

1. _____id

2. _____ow

3. ju_____

4. ha_____

Let's review words that use the letter combinations we have learned. Read each word as I point to it.

strip	straw	sprout
spray	scrub	screw
splash	split	squad
squid	three	throw
edge	judge	itch
hatch		

Let's write a sentence about Charlie and Trike.

Remember to use your best handwriting! Be sure to leave space between your words so that you can read back your sentences easily. It helps to put a finger after each word to see how much space you should leave.

Charlie learned that we can trust the Bible.

Copy the sentence on the lines.

LET'S REVIEW AND APPLY

Let's read the sentence you wrote in the last lesson.

Chårliē learned that we can trŭst the Bīble.

Remember:

- The first word in a sentence begins with a capital letter.
- Sentences end with a period, exclamation point, or question mark.

Did you remember to start your sentence with a capital letter? What punctuation mark did your sentence end with?

Do you remember what kind of a sentence has a period at the end? A sentence that makes a statement or tells something ends with a period. We call this type of sentence a declarative sentence. It declares something. Declare is a word that means to make a statement or to tell something. What do we call a sentence that makes a statement? Yes, it is called a declarative sentence.

Tell me a declarative sentence.

TEACHER NOTE
- The student may need some help coming up with a sentence that ends with a period, a question mark, and an exclamation point. Assist as needed.

Do you remember what kind of a sentence ends in a question mark? A sentence that asks a question ends with a question mark. We call a sentence that asks a question an interrogative sentence. That's a big word! It has the word *interrogate* in it. Interrogate means to question. What do we call a sentence that asks a question? Yes, it is called an interrogative sentence.

Tell me an interrogative sentence.

Do you remember what kind of a sentence ends in an exclamation point? A sentence that shows excitement ends in an exclamation point. We call a sentence that ends with an exclamation point an exclamatory sentence. Exclamatory is a big word, too! It has the word *exclaim* in it. Exclaim means to say something in an excited way. What do we call a sentence that shows excitement? Yes, it is called an exclamatory sentence.

Tell me an exclamatory sentence.

Let's pick some words from *Charlie and Trike in the Grand Canyon Adventure* to use as our spelling words and write them below.

 **TEACHER NOTE**
• Help the student pick 5 short words from pages 18–21 to use as spelling words. If you have trouble picking the words, you may use these words: **trust, strong, kind, thief, smile**. For your reference, be sure to write the words you have chosen in the back of the book in the list of spelling words.

1. _____

2. _____

3. _____

4. _____

5. _____

Study the spelling words you picked out.

Now I am going to read each word to you. Let's see if you can remember how to spell it. It will be fun!

TEACHER NOTE
- Allow the student time to study the words.

- Read each word to the student. The student should spell the word, out loud, without looking. Go back and study the words until he or she can spell them from memory.

- The student may also write each word on an index card to practice. The student may create right-brain flashcards by drawing pictures on the cards or around the letters to help him or her remember how to spell the words.

PICTURE STUDY

Look at the pictures on pages 18–23 of *Charlie and Trike in the Grand Canyon Adventure.*

(1) Describe what is happening on page 18.

(2) What is outside of the tent on page 19?

(3) What is happening inside the tent?

(4) Describe page 20. Include the colors in your description.

(5) What is happening on page 21?

(6) Describe pages 22–23.

Sentence Fun!

Remember, a sentence has two parts.

- The subject tells what or whom the sentence is about.
- The predicate tells what the subject does or is.

I am going to read a sentence to you. Listen carefully.

The girl caught the ball.

What is the subject of the sentence? Yes, the subject is *the girl*. The girl is whom the sentence is about.

Can you tell me what the predicate is? Remember, the predicate tells what the subject does or is. Yes, the predicate is *caught the ball*. We know what the girl did. She caught the ball.

Study each sentence and make sure it has both a subject and predicate. Circle the complete sentences.

1. God loves.

2. We will visit the Grand Canyon.

3. Into the Ark.

4. Water everywhere.

5. The dove gave Noah a branch.

6. God gave us the rainbow.

Circle the correct word in each sentence.

7. The Ark (were, was) built to save Noah, his family, and the animals.

8. Jesus died (to, then) save us.

9. Sin (are, is) doing wrong.

10. We (has, have) to ask Jesus to forgive us.

11. We (can, could) trust the Bible.

12. We (was, will) go to heaven.

Now we have a special surprise! You have done such a great job reading that I have a special book for you to read today. It is called *The Door of Salvation.*

Let's read it!

TEACHER NOTE

- Offer lots of excitement and enthusiasm for all the student has accomplished.

- Offer help if needed, but encourage the student to read it on his or her own. The student may take more than one day to read the book if needed.

- There is a special salvation message in this story. Discuss the story after the student has read it.

 **CREATE YOUR OWN DICTIONARY!**

 **TEACHER NOTE**   • Help the student read the words below.

Let's read the words you can put in your dictionary today.

gift   otter   quick

unlock   vent   view

Remember, for each word you will:

- Find the page that has the same letter your word starts with.
- Write the word on the top line if empty or one of the other lines.
- Draw a picture that shows what the word means.
- Write a simple definition (or meaning) for the word.

Certificate
of
Completion

for

Language Lessons 1

presented to

_____

on this day

_____

Good Job!

How to use this section

These pages are included for the teacher to provide to the student. The teacher may make copies of the practice pages, or they can be laminated (or put in page protectors) and used with dry erase markers.

Phonics Charts are for reference and for further study as needed.

The activities and games are fun ideas to use with lessons or for extra practice.

Table of Contents

How to Hold Your Pencil...234

Grading Options for This Course..234

Course Assessment Chart 235

Recommended Book List for Reading Practice..239

Book Reading List 241

Sight Words...242

Basic Phonics Review...243

Phonics Charts..245

Grammar Study Sheets 253

Spelling List 257

Spelling Words..259

Create Your Own Dictionary! Schedule Word List...262

Create Your Own Dictionary!...263

Activities and Games 327

Alphabet Practice 333

Vowel Practice...337

Consonant Practice 338

Copywork Practice 339

Answer Keys

Worksheet Answers...343

How to Hold Your Pencil

How you hold your pencil can make it easier or harder for you to write letters correctly. Here is one of the best ways to hold your pencil:

- Curl your hand into a loose fist.

- Pick up your pencil and position it between your index finger and your thumb. The back end of the pencil should rest on your hand between the thumb and index finger.

- The weight of the pencil should be resting on your other fingers that are partially curled.

- Press your index finger and thumb against the pencil so it is held securely.

- Start writing!

Assessment

We have included a Course Assessment Chart that covers each week. It may be used for grading purposes.

Grading Options for This Course

It is always the option of an educator to assess student grades however he or she might deem best. For *Language Lessons* the teacher may evaluate whether a student has mastered a particular skill or whether the student needs additional experience. A teacher may rank these on a five-point scale as follows:

Skill Mastered				Needs Experience
5 (equals an A)	4 (B)	3 (C)	2 (D)	1 (equals an F)

A — Student shows complete mastery of concepts with no errors.

B — Student shows mastery of concepts with minimal errors.

C — Student shows partial mastery of concepts. Review of some concepts is needed.

D — Student shows minimal understanding of concepts. Review is needed.

F — Student does not show understanding of concepts. Review is needed.

Course Assessment Chart

	Skill Mastered	Needs Experience
Lesson 1 Reading, Narration, Sight Words Review		
Letter Combinations: *sp, tw, wh, mb, ck, ng, nk*; Alphabet Writing		
Vowels Writing, Silent-e, Long Vowel Sound		
Consonants, Writing		
Dictionary Words (happy, mouse, door, cookie, chair, house)		
Lesson 2 Observation Skills, Reading, Sight Words Review		
Letter Combinations: *sh, ch, qu, ph, dd, ff, ll, ss, tt, zz*; Alphabet Writing		
Vowel Sounds, Picture Study		
Consonants, Writing		
Dictionary Words (dinosaur, dog, sheep, plow, seeds, birds)		
Lesson 3 Reading, Narration, Sight Words Review		
Letter Combinations: *th, kn, lf, lk, y*; Alphabet Writing		
Vowel Sounds, Writing, Picture Study		
Vowel Sounds, Writing		
Dictionary Words (trees, nest, pasture, run, field, oxen)		
Lesson 4 Bible Reading, Narration, Sight Words Review		
Letter Combination: *ea*; Alphabet Writing		
Vowel Sounds, Picture Study		
Vowel Sounds		
Dictionary Words (mud, orchard, fence, wings, sun, moon)		
Lesson 5 Reading, Narration, Sight Words Review		
Letter Combination: *gh*; Spelling Words (bad, cat, men, yes, dip, hit, dog, owl, bud, run)		
Vowel Sounds, Picture Study		
Spelling, Writing, Nouns		
Dictionary Words (stars, bed, hills, wake, yawn, zoo)		
Lesson 6 Observation Skills, Reading, Sight Words Review		
Letter Combinations: *bl, cl, fl, gl, pl, sl*; Letter Writing, Spelling Words (can, cane, bit, bite, pin, pine, not, note, cut, cute)		
Vowel Sounds, Picture Study		
Spelling, Writing, Nouns		
Dictionary Words (breakfast, eat, valley, Noah, Ark, laugh)		
Lesson 7 Reading, Narration, Sight Words Review		
Letter Combinations: *br, cr, dr, fr, gr, pr, tr, wr*; Writing, Spelling Words (laid, maid, seat, meat, tied, lied, boat, coat, fruit, suit)		
Vowel Review, Picture Study		
Spelling, Writing, Nouns		
Dictionary Words (wood, build, flood, grow, under, rain)		

		Skill Mastered	Needs Experience
Lesson 8	Poetry, Rhyming, Narration, Sight Words Review		
	Letter Combination: *ie*; Writing, Spelling (pie, died, field, chief, friend)		
	ie Review, Picture Study		
	Spelling, Writing, Sentence Reading, Nouns and Verbs		
	Dictionary Words (lightning, wind, family, water, walk, rope)		
Lesson 9	Reading, Narration, Sight Words Review		
	Letter Combination: *ei*; Writing, Spelling Words (ceiling, seize, eight, veil, vein)		
	ei Review, Picture Study		
	Spelling, Writing, Sentences, Nouns and Verbs		
	Dictionary Words (cow, float, raven, dove, branch, sing)		
Lesson 10	Reading, Narration, Sight Words Review		
	Letter Combinations: *oy, oi*; Writing, Spelling Words (boy, joy, toy, coin, soil, oink)		
	oy and *oi* Review, Picture Study		
	Spelling, Writing, Sentences, Nouns, Verbs, and Adjectives		
	Dictionary Words (colors, rainbow, sky, apple, mule, tail)		
Lesson 11	Observation Skills, Reading, Sight Words Review		
	Letter Combinations: *ow, ou*; Writing, Spelling Words (loud, mouse, plow, town, flow, grow)		
	ow and *ou* Review, Picture Study		
	Spelling, Writing, Sentences, Nouns, Verbs, and Adjectives		
	Dictionary Words (post, river, Grand Canyon, hand, path, notebook)		
Lesson 12	Reading, Narration, Sight Words Review		
	Letter Combination: *oo*; Writing, Spelling Words (food, moon, boot, cook, foot, wood)		
	oo Review, Picture Study		
	Spelling, Writing, Sentences, Nouns, Verbs, and Adjectives		
	Dictionary Words (cliff, creature, earth, eyes, crab, love)		
Lesson 13	Bible Reading, Narration, Sight Words Review		
	Letter Combination: *ew*; Writing, Spelling Words (blew, few, new, pew, sew)		
	ew Review, Picture Study		
	Spelling, Writing, Sentences, Nouns, Verbs, and Adjectives		
	Dictionary Words (animal, open, queen, in, light, tent)		
Lesson 14	Reading, Narration, Sight Words Review		
	Letter Combination: *ou*; Writing		
	Capitalization, Punctuation, Spelling Words (one, two, three, four, five)		
	Picture Study, Sentences		
	Dictionary Words (edge, day, ant, green, jump, x-ray)		

		Skill Mastered	Needs Experience
Lesson 15	Picture Study, Reading, Narration, Sight Words Review		
	Letter Combinations: *sc, sk, sl, sm, sn, sp, st, sw*; Writing		
	Capitalization, Punctuation, Spelling Words (patch, black, look, green, hand), Picture Study		
	Sentences, Punctuation, Capitalization		
	Dictionary Words (trout, king, iguana, jelly, quack, jeans)		
Lesson 16	Reading, Narration, Sight Words Review		
	Letter Combinations: *al, au, aw, ay, ai, ea, oa, oe, ee*; Writing		
	Capitalization, Punctuation, Spelling Words (time, whole, true, God, Earth), Picture Study		
	Sentences, Punctuation, Capitalization		
	Dictionary Words (insect, umbrella, kid, give, key, quart)		
Lesson 17	Poetry, Rhyming, Narration, Sight Words Review		
	Letter Combinations: *str, spr, scr, spl*; Sentences		
	Capitalization, Punctuation, Spelling Words (coals, next, trout, help, feet) Picture Study		
	Sentences: Subject, Predicate		
	Dictionary Words (ice, up, kick, jungle, net, visit)		
Lesson 18	Reading, Narration, Sight Words Review		
	Letter Combinations: *squ, thr, dge, tch*; Writing		
	Capitalization, Punctuation, Spelling Words (trust, strong, kind, thief, smile) Picture Study		
	Sentences: Subject, Predicate		
	Dictionary Words (otter, view, vent, unlock, quick, gift)		

Recommended Book List for Reading Practice

All books listed are published by Master Books or New Leaf Publishing Group.

Please select books that match your student's reading level. The books in each group are listed alphabetically, not according to the reading level.

Early Learner Board Books

A is for Adam

All God's Children

D is for Dinosaur

Inside Noah's Ark 4 Kids

It's Designed to Do What It Does Do

My Creation Bible

N is for Noah

Remarkable Rescue

The Very Best Plan

When You See a Rainbow

When You See a Star

Early Learner Books Grades K–3

44 Animals of the Bible

Big Thoughts for Little Thinkers — Gospel

Big Thoughts for Little Thinkers — Missions

Big Thoughts for Little Thinkers — Scripture

Big Thoughts for Little Thinkers — Trinity

Charlie & Trike

Cool Creatures of the Ice Age

The Creation Story for Children

Dinosaurs: Stars of the Show

Dinosaurs for Little Kids

The Door of Salvation

God is Really, Really Real

Not Too Small at All

Tower of Babel

The True Account of Adam & Eve

The True Story of Noah's Ark

Whale of a Story

When Dragons' Hearts Were Good

The Work of Your Hand

Grades 4–6 Books

Answers Book for Kids, Vol. 1–8

Dinosaurs by Design

Dinosaurs for Kids

Dinosaurs of Eden

Dry Bones and Other Fossils

God's Amazing Creatures and Me

How Many Animals Were on the Ark?

Inside Noah's Ark — Why it Worked

Life in the Great Ice Age

Marvels of Creation — Birds

Marvels of Creation — Mammals

Marvels of Creation — Sea Creatures

Men of Science, Men of God

Noah's Ark and the Ararat Adventure

Noah's Ark: Thinking Outside the Box

Operation Rawhide

The Story of In God We Trust

The Story of The Pledge of Allegiance

What's so Hot about the Sun?

Why Is Keiko Sick?

Grades 7–8 Books

The 10 Minute Bible Journey

The Building of the ARK Encounter

Champions of Invention

Champions of Mathematics

Champions of Science

Dragons of the Deep

Footprints in the Ash

The Great Alaskan Dinosaur Adventure

Great for God

If Animals Could Talk

Life Before Birth

Quick Answers to Tough Questions

Uncovering the Mysteries of the
   Woolly Mammoth

Book Reading List

Be sure to keep a record of the books your student is reading. There are spaces below for title, author, and the date of completion. It can be a positive experience as the student sees this list being filled in and knows that he or she is mastering the important skill of reading. It can be helpful to know the authors and/or specific topics your student expresses interest in by allowing him or her to help make choices in selecting books. These selections should be fun for the student!

Book Title	Author	Date Completed

Sight Words

- a
- all
- an
- and
- are
- as
- at
- be
- belong
- but
- by
- can
- did
- for
- from
- get
- had
- has

- have
- he
- his
- how
- I
- if
- in
- is
- it
- my
- no
- not
- of
- on
- or
- out
- see
- she

- so
- than
- that
- the
- them
- then
- they
- this
- to
- was
- we
- what
- when
- who
- will
- you

Basic Phonics Review

Vowels can make different sounds. We sometimes use symbols to help us remember what sound the vowel is making in a word.

A vowel can make the short sound. Example: ă as in dăd.

A vowel can make the long sound. The long vowel sound says its name. Example: ā as in cāpe.

Study the chart to review different sounds vowels can make.

Vowel	As In
ă	dad
ā	cape
å	far
ĕ	men
ē	be
ĭ	sit
ī	like

Vowel	As In
ŏ	not
ō	bone
ŭ	sun
ū	use

Optional:

Some teachers may want to introduce the schwa sound to their students. *Foundations Phonics* and the *Language Lessons for a Living Education* series do not cover this sound until dictionary pronunciations are covered in Level 5. Instead, schwa sound words are listed among sight words.

All vowels can make the schwa sound. The schwa sound makes a sound like the short-u sound. It sounds like /uh/. The symbol for the schwa sound is an upside-down e: ə

Those who wish to introduce the schwa sound may use this chart:

Vowel	As In	Example
a	was	wəs
e	the	thə
i	family	faməly
o	gallon	gallən

Phonics Charts

Phonics reviewed and learned in *Language Lessons 1*:

Letters	Sounds Like	As In	Read
sp	/sp/	spout	spĭn
tw	/tw/	twin	twĭg
wh	/w/	whale	whĭp
⚠ wh	/h/	whole	who
mb	/m/	comb	lămb
ck	/ck/	sick	dŭck
ng	/ng/	wing	sŏng
nk	/nk/	wink	sĭnk
sh	/sh/	ship	shŏp
ch	/ch/	child	chĭp

The ⚠ means the sound is an exception to the rule.

Letters	Sounds Like	As In	Read
qu	/qu/	quilt	quĭz
ph	/f/	phone	phōtō
dd	/d/	add	ŏdd
ff	/f/	puff	cŭff
ll	/l/	llama	båll
ss	/s/	kiss	mĕss
tt	/t/	mitt	mŭtt
zz	/z/	fizz	bŭzz
th	/th/	this	thăt
th	/th/	thanks	thĭnk
kn	/n/	knit	knŏt

Letters	Sounds Like	As In	Read
lf	/f/	calf	hălf
lk	/k/	walk	tålk
y	/y/	yak	yĕs
y	/ī/	sky	spy
y	/ē/	lady	bāby
⚠ u	/oo/	glue	tube
ea	/ĕ/	bread	hĕad
ea	/ē/	beam	sēat
gh	/g/	aghast	ghōst
gh	/f/	rough	lăugh
gh	silent	dough	hīgh

The ⚠ means the sound is an exception to the rule.

Letters	Sounds Like	As In	Read
ou	/oo/	could	would
ou	/ü/	through	croup
ou	/ō/	four	your
ou	/ŭ/	enough	touch
bl	/bl/	block	blŭsh
cl	/cl/	clock	clăp
fl	/fl/	flock	flăg
gl	/gl/	globe	glăd
pl	/pl/	plant	plŭm
sl	/sl/	slide	slĕd
br	/br/	brick	brŭsh

Letters	Sounds Like	As In	Read
cr	/cr/	crate	crăb
dr	/dr/	dress	drŭm
fr	/fr/	fruit	frŏg
gr	/gr/	grape	grŭb
pr	/pr/	prize	prĕss
tr	/tr/	trick	trăsh
wr	/wr/	write	wrăp
oy	/oy/	boy	joy
oi	/oy/	coin	soil
ou	/ow/	loud	mouse
ow	/ow/	plow	town

Letters	Sounds Like	As In	Read
⚠ ow	/ō/	flow	grōw
oo	/oo/	food	moon
oo	/oo/	cook	foot
ew	/oo/	new	blew
ew	/ū/	view	few
⚠ ew	/ō/	sew	
sc	/sc/	scout	scår
sk	/sk/	skate	skŭnk
sl	/sl/	sling	slīme
sm	/sm/	smell	smōke
sn	/sn/	snow	snăp

The ⚠ means the sound is an exception to the rule.

Letters	Sounds Like	As In	Read
sp	/sp/	spot	spĕnd
st	/st/	stop	stĭng
sw	/sw/	swing	swĭm
al	/aw/	talk	walk
au	/aw/	haul	autō
aw	/aw/	draw	claw
ay	/ā/	play	pray
ai	/ā/	pain	mail
ea	/ē/	bean	peach
oa	/ō/	boat	toad
oe	/ō/	toe	foe

Letters	Sounds Like	As In	Read
ee	/ē/	deer	seed
str	/str/	strip	straw
spr	/spr/	sprout	spray
scr	/scr/	scrub	screw
spl	/spl/	splash	split
squ	/squ/	squad	squid
thr	/thr/	three	throw
dge	/j/	edge	judge
tch	/ch/	itch	hatch

Phonics Rules

The silent-e at the end of the word makes the vowel say its name. We call this the long vowel sound.

When we have a vowel pair in the middle of a word, sometimes the second vowel is silent and makes the first vowel say its name.

The vowels *ie* can follow the rule and make the long-i sound. We see this in the words *pie* and *died*.

The vowels *ie* can trade with each other! Instead of the second vowel being silent and the first vowel saying its name, the FIRST vowel is silent, and the SECOND vowel says its name. That means the *i* stays silent and the *e* says its name! We see this in the words *field* and *chief*.

The vowels *ie* can be quite tricky and make the short-e sound. That is very tricky, isn't it? We see this in the word *friend*.

i before *e* except after *c*, or when sounding like *a* as in *neighbor* and *weigh*. With the vowels *ei*, the silent *i* makes the *e* say its name.

Some words end with the letters *ed*. In many words that end in *ed*, only the /d/ sound is heard. In some words, the letters *ed* sound like /ed/.

The means the sound is an exception to the rule.

About Books

Author: the person who wrote the book is the author.

Illustrator: the person who drew the pictures in the book is the illustrator.

Grammar

The vowels are a, e, i, o, u, and sometimes y.

The consonants are b, c, d, f, g, h, j, k, l, m, n, p, q, r, s, t, v, w, x, y, and z.

Words that are things are called nouns. A noun can be a person. A noun can also be a place.

A noun names a person, place, or thing.

Verbs show action.

An adjective describes a noun. An adjective can be a color or can tell about size, texture, or shape. An adjective can also tell how many and how something smells, tastes, or sounds. An adjective can be a color or can tell about size, texture, or shape. An adjective can also tell how many and how something smells, tastes, or sounds.

Two words that rhyme sound the same at the end of the word.

Words and Sentences

When we write a person's name, we use a capital letter for the first letter.

When we write the name of a city, state, or country, we use a capital letter for the first letter. Example: Dayton, Ohio
Some places have a name that includes more than one word. Each word beings with a capital letter. Example: Grand Canyon

The first word in a sentence begins with a capital letter and end with punctuation. Punctuation can be a period, exclamation point, or question mark.

A sentence must end in a punctuation mark:

a period **.**   question mark **?**   exclamation point **!**

A declarative sentence makes a statement, or tells something, and ends in a period.

Sentences that say something exciting end in an exclamation point. An exclamation point looks like this: **!**

Sentences that ask a question end in a question mark. A question mark looks like this: **?**

A sentence has two parts. It has a subject and a predicate.

The subject is often the first part of a sentence and tells what or whom the sentence is about. Every sentence has a subject.

The predicate tells what the subject does or is.

Spelling List

On the following pages are the spelling words from each lesson. You may choose to write out the words below that the student needs additional work on and to share this list with the student. Then you can work on those words together.

1. _____

2. _____

3. _____

4. _____

5. _____

6. _____

7. _____

8. _____

9. _____

10. _____

11. _____

12. _____

13. _____

14. _____

15. _____

16. _____

17. _____

18. _____

19. _____

20. _____

21. _____

22. _____

23. _____

24. _____

25. _____

26. _____

27. _____

28. _____

29. _____

30. _____

Spelling Words

Please note the spelling words in this course do not begin until Lesson 5.

Lesson 5

- bad
- bud
- cat
- dip
- dog
- hit
- men
- owl
- run
- yes

Lesson 6

- bit
- bite
- can
- cane
- cut

- cute
- not
- note
- pin
- pine

Lesson 7

- laid
- maid
- seat
- meat
- tied
- lied
- boat
- coat
- fruit
- suit

Lesson 8

- died
- pie
- chief
- field
- friend

Lesson 9

- ceiling
- eight
- seize
- veil
- vein

Lesson 10

- boy
- coin
- joy
- oink
- toy
- soil

Lesson 11

- flow
- grow
- loud
- mouse
- plow
- town

Lesson 12

- boot
- cook
- food
- foot
- moon
- wood

Lesson 13

- blew
- few
- new
- pew
- sew

Lesson 14

- one
- two
- three
- four
- five
- _____
- _____
- _____
- _____
- _____

Lesson 15

- black
- green
- hand
- look
- patch
- _____
- _____
- _____
- _____
- _____

Lesson 16

- Earth
- God
- time
- true
- whole

- _____
- _____
- _____
- _____
- _____

Lesson 17

- coals
- feet
- help
- next
- trout
- _____
- _____
- _____
- _____
- _____

Lesson 18

- kind
- smile
- strong
- thief
- trust
- _____
- _____
- _____
- _____
- _____

Create Your Own Dictionary! Schedule Word List

Lesson 1
1. chair
2. cookie
3. door
4. happy
5. house
6. mouse

Lesson 2
1. birds
2. dinosaur
3. dog
4. plow
5. seeds
6. sheep

Lesson 3
1. field
2. nest
3. oxen
4. pasture
5. run
6. trees

Lesson 4
1. fence
2. moon
3. mud
4. orchard
5. sun
6. wings

Lesson 5
1. bed
2. hills
3. stars
4. wake
5. yawn
6. zoo

Lesson 6
1. Ark
2. breakfast
3. eat
4. laugh
5. Noah
6. valley

Lesson 7
1. build
2. flood
3. grow
4. rain
5. under
6. wood

Lesson 8
1. family
2. lightning
3. rope
4. walk
5. water
6. wind

Lesson 9
1. branch
2. cow
3. dove
4. float
5. raven
6. sing

Lesson 10
1. apple
2. colors
3. mule
4. rainbow
5. sky
6. tail

Lesson 11
1. Grand Canyon
2. hand
3. notebook
4. path
5. post
6. river

Lesson 12
1. cliff
2. crab
3. creature
4. earth
5. eyes
6. love

Lesson 13
1. animal
2. in
3. light
4. open
5. queen
6. tent

Lesson 14
1. ant
2. day
3. edge
4. green
5. jump
6. x-ray

Lesson 15
1. iguana
2. jeans
3. jelly
4. king
5. quack
6. trout

Lesson 16
1. give
2. insect
3. key
4. kid
5. quart
6. umbrella

Lesson 17
1. ice
2. jungle
3. kick
4. net
5. up
6. visit

Lesson 18
1. gift
2. otter
3. quick
4. unlock
5. vent
6. view

my own dictionary

by

_____

Creating Your Dictionary Pages

Remember: The first letter of each of your spelling words will determine which dictionary page you will use.

- Find that letter page in your dictionary.
- Write your spelling word on the first line.
- Draw a picture of what the spelling word means to you.
- Then, write a simple definition (or meaning) for the spelling word.

For example, let's do a page for the word *happy*.

The word *happy* begins with the letter H. Let's find the "H" section in our dictionary pages. The dictionary pages are in alphabetical order. It may help to sing the Alphabet Song when you are trying to find the correct page.

Did you find the H page?

- Write the word *happy* on the top line.
- Draw a picture that shows what *happy* means.
- Write a simple definition (or meaning) for the word *happy*. In our example, we wrote the word "joyful" because joyful means happy.

TEACHER NOTE
- Let the student's stamina determine how many words are added to the dictionary each week. Also, the student may prefer to write the word and draw a picture. If the student writes a definition, it should consist of one to three words.

my own dictionary

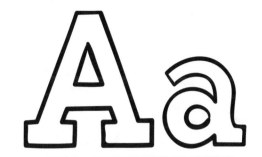

Language Level 1 – Create Your Own Dictionary!

my own dictionary

Bb

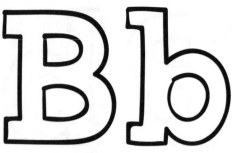

Language Level 1 – Create Your Own Dictionary!

my own dictionary

Bb

Language Level 1 – Create Your Own Dictionary!

my own dictionary

Cc

my own dictionary

Cc

Language Level 1 – Create Your Own Dictionary!

my own dictionary

Dd

Language Level 1 – Create Your Own Dictionary!

my own dictionary

Dd

my own dictionary

Ee

Ff

Language Level 1 – Create Your Own Dictionary!

my own dictionary

Ff

Ff

Language Level 1 – Create Your Own Dictionary!

my own dictionary

Gg

Language Level 1 – Create Your Own Dictionary!

my own dictionary

Gg

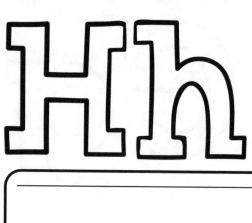

Language Level 1 – Create Your Own Dictionary!

my own dictionary

Hh

Ii

Language Level 1 – Create Your Own Dictionary!

my own dictionary

Ii

Language Level 1 – Create Your Own Dictionary!

my own dictionary

J j

Kk

Language Level 1 – Create Your Own Dictionary!

my own dictionary

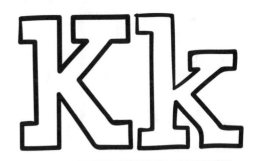

L1

Language Level 1 – Create Your Own Dictionary!

my own dictionary

Ll

Mm

Language Level 1 – Create Your Own Dictionary!

my own dictionary

Mm

Nn

Language Level 1 – Create Your Own Dictionary!

my own dictionary

Nn

Language Level 1 – Create Your Own Dictionary!

my own dictionary

Oo

Pp

Language Level 1 – Create Your Own Dictionary!

my own dictionary

Pp

Language Level 1 – Create Your Own Dictionary!

my own dictionary

Qq

Language Level 1 – Create Your Own Dictionary!

my own dictionary

Rr

Rr

Language Level 1 – Create Your Own Dictionary!

my own dictionary

Ss

Language Level 1 – Create Your Own Dictionary!

my own dictionary

Tt

Language Level 1 – Create Your Own Dictionary!

my own dictionary

Tt

Language Level 1 – Create Your Own Dictionary!

my own dictionary

Uu

Language Level 1 – Create Your Own Dictionary!

my own dictionary

V v

Language Level 1 – Create Your Own Dictionary!

my own dictionary

Ww

Ww

Language Level 1 – Create Your Own Dictionary!

my own dictionary

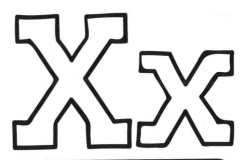

Language Level 1 – Create Your Own Dictionary!

my own dictionary

Zz

Language Level 1 – Create Your Own Dictionary!

my own dictionary

Language Level 1 – Create Your Own Dictionary!

These games and activities are meant to add extra practice and fun to the lessons. They are optional, but most students will want to do as many as they can. We have included many variations of the Memory Matching Game to encourage short-term memory skills since they are crucial to reading comprehension. We have also included games with new topics to prepare the student for Level 2.

We encourage the student to create the cards used in the games. Writing out the words on the cards is part of the learning process.

Supplies:

- Index cards
- Markers, crayons, stickers, etc.
- Three-hole punch and rings, or clips to store index cards (optional)

Simon Says

Focus:

- Nouns, Adjectives, Verbs, Auditory Perception, Physical Activity

Number of Players:

- Two or more

Game Play:

- Decide if the students should sit for nouns, verbs, or adjectives. Each student should stand in front of a chair. "Simon" stands facing the students. Simon says a either a noun, verb, or adjective. The students should sit when the chosen word type is said by Simon. If the students sit when they should stand (or vice versa), they are out. The last student standing wins. Pick a new Simon and play again!

Game Variation:

- When there are only two players, track how many nouns the player gets right in a row. Work to beat the highest record.

Days of the Week (Months of the Year) Memory

Focus:

- Days of the Week, Months of the Year, Memory, Syllables

Number of Players:

- One or more

Game Play:

- Have students write the names of the week on index cards — one day per card.

- Ask students what they do on Sunday. Have them draw it on a card. Continue with the remaining weeks until they have 14 cards — seven with the names of the week and seven with what they do each day.

- Turn the cards over and arrange them and play the memory game, matching the days with the students' drawings.

- When the game is over, have the students arrange the days of the week in order.

Bonus Challenge:

- Each time a student turns over a Day of the Week card, have him or her clap the syllables as he or she reads it.

Game Variation:

- Repeat using the Months of the Year. Have students draw weather-related pictures for each month, including things they do.

Alphabet Memory

Focus:

- Alphabet, Memory

Number of Players:

- One or more

Game Play:

- Ask the student to write a capital *A* on a notecard. Next, have the student write a lowercase *a* on a notecard. Continue in this manner until all the uppercase and lowercase letters are written on the notecards.

- Mix up the notecards.

- Turn the notecards over and arrange them on the floor, a desk, or table.

- Each player turns two cards over, trying to find a match. If the player finds a match, he or she goes again. If not, the next person takes a turn.

- When the game is over, the person with the most matches wins.

Bonus Challenges:

- Have players arrange all the letters in the order of the alphabet.

- Have players find something around the house that begins with each letter of the alphabet.

Game Variations:

- Each time a letter is turned over, the student must say a word that starts with that letter.

- Each time a letter is turned over, the student must state whether it is a vowel or a consonant.

I Spy

Focus:

- Alphabet, Nouns, Adjectives, Observation

Number of Players:

- Two or more

Game Play:

- The "spy" says, "I spy with my little eyes something . . ." then goes on to describe an object (noun) that is in the room.

- The other players try to guess what noun the person has spied by asking questions such as "Is it red?" "Is it something you wear?"

- The game ends when the noun is discovered.

Game Variations:

- The spy finds objects that start with different letters of the alphabet. He or she would say, "I spy with my little eyes something that begins with the letter *a*." Vowel sounds and blends may also be used.

- The spy must use adjectives to describe the object.

- Give each player a sheet of paper. Have the students create three columns by writing "person," "place," and "thing" across the top of the page. Each time a noun is discovered, have the students write the word under the correct column.

- Have the students write down the adjectives used. When the game is over, have them group the adjectives according to type, color, size, etc.

Charades

Focus:

- Action Verbs, Physical Activity

Number of Players:

- Two or more

Game Play:

- Have the student write a different action verb on at least ten index cards. Mix them up and put them in a pile, face down.
- Have the student draw a card and act out the verb.
- The teacher must guess the verb.
- Take turns being the actor until all the students and the teacher have had a turn and/or all the cards are used.

Game Variations:

- Set a timer when the actor begins. Track how fast the player can guess the verb. Work to beat the quickest time.
- Divide players into teams. When it is their turn, the team picks a teammate to be the actor.

Drawing Game

Focus:

- Subject, Predicate, Sentences, Creativity, Hand-Eye Coordination

Number of Players:

- Two or more

Game Play:

- Ask students to make two stacks of cards. Each stack should have at least eight cards, equal in number. On the back side of the cards in one stack, write the word "Subject." Write "Predicate" on the back of the second stack.

- Ask the students to write sentences, except they will write the Subject part on one card and the Predicate part on the other.

- Shuffle the Subject stack then shuffle the Predicate stack.

- The first player takes a card from each stack. The player must draw the sentence for the other players to guess.

Game Variations:

- Set a timer when the player begins to draw. Track how fast the others can guess the sentence. Work to beat the quickest time.

- Divide players into teams. When it is their turn, the team picks a teammate to draw the sentence.

Alphabet Practice

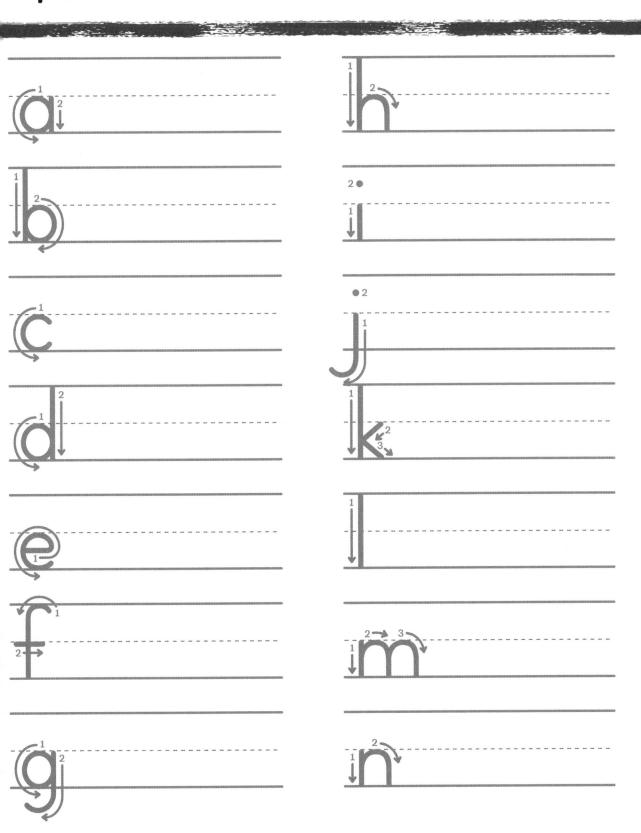

Language Level 1 – Alphabet Practice

Alphabet Practice

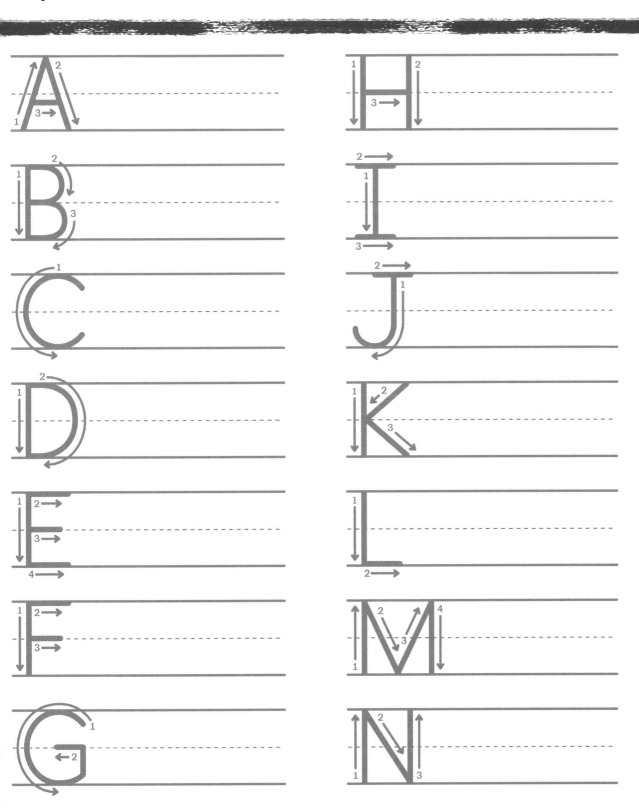

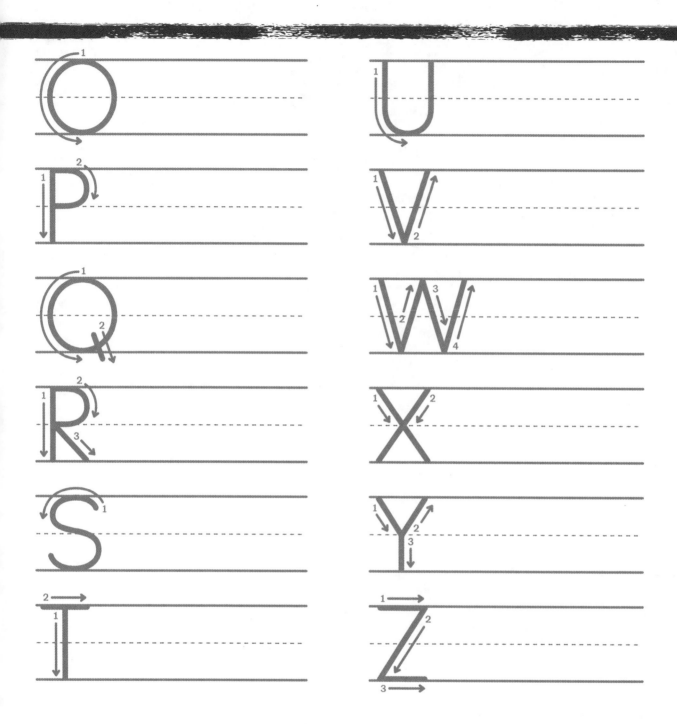

Language Level 1 – Alphabet Practice

Vowel Practice

a

o

e

u

i

a

o

e

u

i

Consonant Practice

b c d f g h j k l m n

p q r s t v w x y z

Copywork Practice

(1) A noun is a person, place, or thing.

(2) Verbs show action.

(3) An adjective describes a noun.

(4) The first word in a sentence begins with a capital letter.

(5) Sentences end with a period, exclamation point, or question mark.

(6) The subject tells what or whom the sentence is about.

(7) The predicate tells what the subject does or is.

Language Level 1 – Copywork Practice

Answer Keys

Answers for the numbered problems are provided here
with the exception of the Narration Practice questions
and select Spelling Lessons.

Language Lessons for a Living Education Level 1 ⚬ Worksheet Answer Keys

Answers are given for numbered problems on the worksheets.

Lesson 1; Exercise 2; Day 2

1. spin
2. twig
3. whip
4. lamb
5. duck
6. song
7. sink

Lesson 1; Exercise 4; Day 4

1. ball
2. fan
3. cat
4. gum
5. dog
6. hat
7. jar
8. hen
9. key
10. doll
11. lip
12. sun

Lesson 2; Exercise 2; Day 7

1. shop
2. chip
3. quiz
4. photo
5. odd
6. cuff
7. ball
8. mess
9. mutt
10. buzz

Lesson 2; Exercise 4; Day 9

1. man
2. quilt
3. nut
4. rug
5. pan
6. sad
7. tub
8. fox
9. van
10. yak
11. web
12. zip

Lesson 3; Exercise 2; Day 12

1. that
2. think
3. knot
4. half
5. talk
6. yes
7. spy
8. baby

Lesson 3; Exercise 4; Day 14

1. pan
2. tape
3. car
4. web
5. key
6. pin
7. ice
8. phone
9. fox
10. sun
11. cube
12. tube

Lesson 4; Exercise 2; Day 17

1. head
2. seat

Lesson 4; Exercise 4; Day 19

1. ī
2. ŏ
3. ā
4. ĭ
5. ŏ
6. ĕ
7. ă
8. ē
9. ŭ
10. ō
11. å
12. ŭ

Just 4 Fun!

Lesson 5; Exercise 2; Day 22

1. tough
2. high
3. gherkin

Lesson 5; Exercise 3; Day 23

Just 4 Fun!

Lesson 5; Exercise 4; Day 24

1. dip
2. men
3. hit
4. dog
5. bad
6. run
7. cat
8. yes
9. bud
10. owl
11. brush, cat, frog, doll, dog, toy

Just 4 Fun!

    6

Lesson 6; Exercise 2; Day 27

1. blush
2. clap
3. flag
4. glad
5. plum
6. sled
7. cane
8. bite
9. pine
10. note
11. cute

Lesson 6; Exercise 3; Day 28

Just 4 Fun!

Lesson 6; Exercise 4; Day 29

1. bite
2. pin
3. can
4. not
5. cute
6. note
7. pine
8. cane
9. bit
10. cut
11. man, friend, maid, boat, fruit

Just 4 Fun!

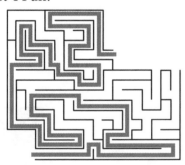

Lesson 7; Exercise 2; Day 32

1. brush
2. crab
3. drum
4. frog
5. grub
6. press
7. trash
8. wrap

Lesson 7; Exercise 3; Day 33

Just 4 Fun!

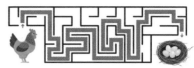

hen, nest

Lesson 7; Exercise 4; Day 34

1. tied
2. coat
3. fruit
4. maid
5. meat
6. seat
7. boat
8. suit
9. lied
10. laid
11. lake, smile, zoo, canyon, bud, field

Lesson 8; Exercise 4; Day 39

1. chief
2. died
3. friend
4. pie
5. field
6. Dad waved a flag.
7. Sam drove the car.
8. Mom looked at the stars.
9. Jess chewed gum.
10. Dan wore a vest.
11. barked
12. walk, throw, press, grow

Lesson 9; Exercise 4; Day 44

1. eight
2. seize
3. veil

4. vein

5. ceiling

6. Joe ate the cheese.

7. Sally gave me a treat.

8. Mommy will weigh the fruit.

9. Daddy made lunch.

10. The toast is hot.

11. cook, raining, planting, seize, yawn, look

Lesson 10; Exercise 4; Day 49

1. coin

2. toy

3. boy

4. oink

5. soil

6. joy

7. The (goat, gate) ate the grass.

8. The woman (planted, salted) a garden.

9. The child (ate, picked) the flower.

10. The stone (is, did) heavy.

11. The stars (shoe, shine) at night.

12. brown

13. big, two, red, happy, blue

Just 4 Fun!

Lesson 11; Exercise 4; Day 54

1. flow

2. grow

3. loud

4. town

5. mouse

6. plow

7. The mouse (rain, ran) from the cat.

8. The camel (drank, drink) from the bowl.

9. The tiger (lost, lived) in the jungle.

10. The ant (worked, walked) all summer.

11. The pig (reads, likes) to roll in mud.

12. fast, blue, three, small

Lesson 12; Exercise 4; Day 59

1. boot

2. wood

3. foot

4. food

5. moon

6. cook

7. The cat (food, roof) dish was full.

8. The shining (spoon, moon) lit up the sky.

9. The owl began to (scoot, hoot) at night.

10. Wear a (hood, good) because it's cold.

11. The man started to (book, cook) our food.

12. Nouns: cow, car, song, ball

13. Verbs: read, walk, sat, bake

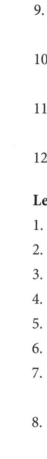

14. Adjectives: hot, long, nine, red

Lesson 13; Exercise 4; Day 64

1. pew
2. new
3. few
4. sew
5. blew
6. I will (stank, stack) the blocks.
7. You (blink, blank) your eyes.
8. They (look, like) milk to drink.
9. He (swims, saves) in the pool.
10. She has (saved, jumped) her coins.
11. Nouns: milk, coins, blocks, pool
12. Verbs: stack, swim, save, look
13. Adjectives: cold, green, salty, gold

Lesson 14; Exercise 2; Day 67

1. would
2. croup
3. your
4. touch

Lesson 14; Exercise 4; Day 69

1. Dad went to work.
2. Cars drive fast.
3. Dogs like to bark.
4. Fish can swim.
5. Barns are for animals.

Lesson 15; Exercise 2; Day 72

1. scar
2. skunk
3. slime

4. smoke
5. snap
6. spend
7. sting
8. swim

Lesson 15; Exercise 4; Day 74

1. Mom pets the cat.
2. Where are you going?
3. Come here quickly!
4. Birds can fly.
5. Get out of the way!
6. Who is going with us?
7. We took a trip to (New York, ohio).
8. (david, Jess) went to church.
9. (I, i) like to read books.
10. We can go to the (Zoo, zoo).
11. We will go to the city of (Erie, erie).

Just 4 Fun!

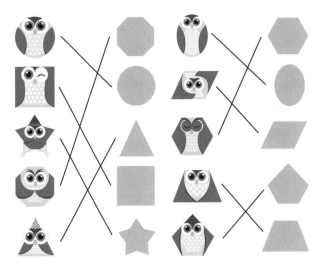

owl, hoot

Lesson 16; Exercise 2; Day 77

1. walk
2. auto
3. claw
4. pray

5. mail

6. peach

7. toad

8. foe

9. seed

Lesson 16; Exercise 4; Day 79

1. Where did you go?

2. My mom gave me a hug.

3. Who lost their coat?

4. I did it!

5. That is hot!

6. My dog likes to run.

7. Where did (Charlie, charlie) go?

8. (God, god) loves me.

9. We learn about (jesus, Jesus) at church.

10. The (Boy, boy) sat next to me.

11. My church is on (main, Main) Street.

Just 4 Fun!

> tennis ball
> football
> beach ball
> tennis ball

Lesson 17; Exercise 2; Day 82

1. straw

2. spray

3. screw

4. split

Lesson 17; Exercise 4; Day 84

1. Charlie kicked a rock.

2. Ate the apple.

3. Swings the rope.

4. I went outside to play.

5. We ate soup for lunch.

6. We (had, has) a fun time at the park.

7. We (are, have) going to church.

8. He (baking, baked) a cake.

9. He (swims, saves) in the pool.

10. I (were, was) going to take the dog for a walk.

Lesson 18; Exercise 2; Day 87

1. squid

2. throw

3. judge

4. hatch

Lesson 18; Exercise 4; Day 89

1. God loves.

2. We will visit the Grand Canyon.

3. Into the Ark.

4. Water everywhere.

5. The dove gave Noah a branch.

6. God gave us the rainbow.

7. The Ark (were, was) built to save Noah, his family, and the animals.

8. Jesus died (to, then) save us.

9. Sin (are, is) doing wrong.

10. We (has, have) to ask Jesus to forgive us.

11. We (can, could) trust the Bible.

12. We (was, will) go to heaven.

Language Lessons for a Living Education

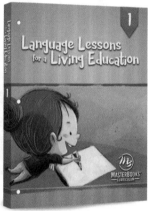

GRADE 1
LANGUAGE LESSONS FOR A LIVING EDUCATION 1

978-1-68344-211-0

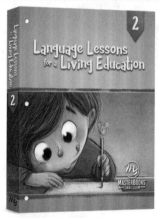

GRADE 2
LANGUAGE LESSONS FOR A LIVING EDUCATION 2

978-1-68344-122-9

GRADE 3
LANGUAGE LESSONS FOR A LIVING EDUCATION 3

978-1-68344-137-3

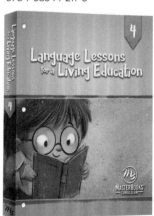

GRADE 4
LANGUAGE LESSONS FOR A LIVING EDUCATION 4

978-1-68344-138-0

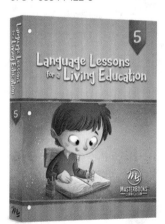

GRADE 5
LANGUAGE LESSONS FOR A LIVING EDUCATION 5

978-1-68344-178-6

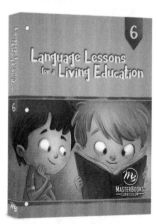

GRADE 6
LANGUAGE LESSONS FOR A LIVING EDUCATION 6

978-1-68344-209-7